CW00403904

For my

LOVELY MUM

beautiful

smart

gorgeous

-fab!-

Purple Ronnie

summersdale

FOR MY LOVELY MUM

Summersdale Publishers Ltd
46 West Street
Chichester
West Sussex
PO19 1RP
UK

www.summersdale.com

www.purpleronnie.com

Printed and bound in the Czech Republic

ISBN: 978-1-84953-876-3

Substantial discounts on bulk quantities of Summersdale books are available to corporations, professional associations and other organisations. For details contact Nicky Douglas by telephone: +44 (0) 1243 756902, fax: +44 (0) 1243 786300 or email: nicky@summersdale.com.

To....................................

From....................................

Being a mum is a busy job
With so many things to do
But if I could choose the
world's BEST MUM
I'd definitely pick you

made by
mum x

Mums are the best at making things!

Where would I
be without you
as my P.A.?

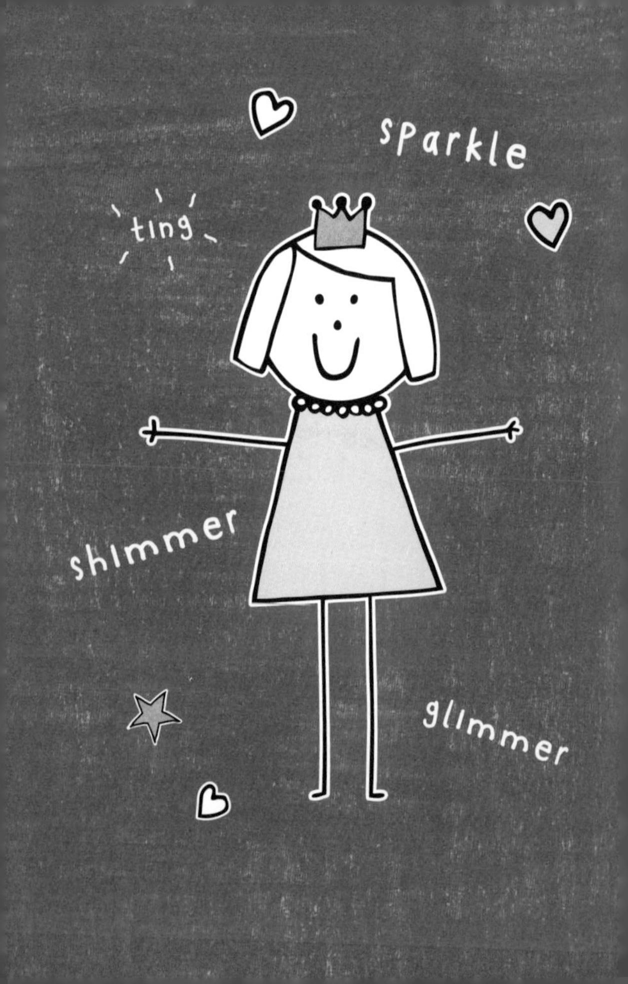
sparkle
ting
shimmer
glimmer

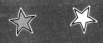

Queen Mum!

On Mother's Day I'll spoil you
With crumpets and tea in bed
The biggest bunch of flowers
And a crown for your head

You're always there for me
Even when I raid the fridge
Or hog the sofa and TV!

You make caring an art form

You ACE the
showstoppers
every time!

Why don't you put your feet up
And take the day off too
Cos it must be very hard to be
A mum as GREAT as you

'OMG... my mum
is trending'

#no1mum

#cool

Where would I be without you?

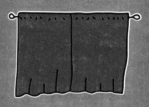

Still in bed, probably...

You're the BEST MUM ever
And a demon baker too!
You're always kind and caring
And that's why I love YOU

I love our girly shopping trips — especially as you always get me loads of brilliant treats!

Me feeling sorry
for myself...

... Me after a call
from you!

Has anyone told you lately
How AWESOME you really are?
If not, let me shout
from the rooftops
You're the brightest
shining STAR!

celebrate

Let's raise a glass to mums everywhere!

YIPPEE!

I'm still your little angel
I think you will agree
And even when I
mess things up
I know you're there for me

You still know how to party,
Your dancing is so cool,
When you spin and shimmy
My mates think
'This mum rules!'

Don't mind me while
I make off with
your best heels!

I don't always show
my best side...

... but you bring out
the best in me!

When you give me a
great big hug
Everything seems better
My huffs or heartaches
melt away
You're like a snuggly sweater

If mums were flowers,
I'd pick you

Good Mum Checklist

three spare packs of tissues (for teary chats)

extra lippy (for embarrassing kisses)

a sweet treat
(that's been
nibbled)

a spare
scarf
(in case
you feel
the chills)

You'll always be my hero
You're so stylish and so fun
There's no better way
to say it than —
You're a completely
brilliant mum!

You always give me good advice — even when I don't want to hear it!

You always know best

Though I pretend your
jokes are cringe
And your stories aren't
that great,

I secretly reuse them
When I'm chatting
with my mates

I'm still your child,

however old I get...

My idea of a hearty breakfast

Your idea of a hearty breakfast

You're barrels of fun
and lovely as well

You really couldn't
be greater

Sit down, relax and
put your feet up

Tonight I'll be
your waiter!

I don't need an
alarm clock when
I've got you!

You treating me

Me trying to treat you

You're magic and
you're awesome
You're fab and funny too
I think you're really super
There's no better
mum than you!

IOU

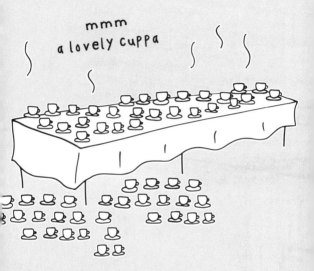

about a billion cups of tea

Me in the eyes
of the world

perfection

Me in the eyes of Mum

I love our get-togethers
When we natter over tea
You always put my
world to rights
With a Chelsea bun, or three

You're always
there in my
hour of need!

What you think your phone volume is

What your phone volume actually is

YAY!
PROBS

♡

When I'm struggling
with my problems
We go through them one by one
And you always have the answers
Cos you ain't half clever, Mum!

♡

MUM: a little word with a BIG meaning

Fun times with Mum
The night before...

... The next morning

When I can't find
my bits and bobs
And I've been looking
round for days,

#Melfietime!

Life skills my mum has taught me

saying please and thank you – except when someone cuts you up on the motorway

look after your appearance – especially shoes and nails, as you never know who you're going to meet

If you don't have anything nice to say, put a sock in it (but make it a clean one!)

make do and mend

If I were a top-level doctor
Helping people in a state,

I'd prescribe them a
large dose of my mum
Because you always
make things great!

No one can
embarrass me
like you can!

You always know
what I'm doing

It's like you have
a sixth sense

Sometimes it's
for my benefit

Sometimes to
my expense!

PURPLE RONNIE

PurpleRonnieWorld · · · · · · · purpleronnie.com

@purple_ronnie

You Tube PurpleRonnieOfficial

coolabi

If you're interested in finding out more
about our books, find us on Facebook
at **Summersdale Publishers** and follow
us on Twitter at **@Summersdale**.

www.summersdale.com

CAPTIVE

Sister Catherine Grainger knows that the Bellington
District General Hospital is lucky to have the services of their new consultant, Johnnie Kirkland. She
also knows the hospital is not big enough for both of
them and she will have to go!

Books you will enjoy
in our Doctor–Nurse series

HOSPITAL ACROSS THE BRIDGE by Lisa Cooper
BACHELOR DOCTOR by Sonia Deane
NEW SURGEON AT ST LUCIAN'S by Elizabeth Houghton
THE SURGEON'S WIFE by Judith Worthy
ANGEL IN PARADISE by Lindsay Hicks
DOCTORS DON'T CRY by Elizabeth Gilzean
ACROSS THE PEARL RIVER by Zara Holman
THE SURGEON'S QUEST by Elizabeth Petty
VISITING CONSULTANT by Betty Neels
FLYAWAY SISTER by Lisa Cooper
TROPICAL NURSE by Margaret Barker
LADY IN HARLEY STREET by Anne Vinton
FIRST-YEAR'S FANCY by Lynne Collins
DESERT FLOWER by Dana James
INDIAN OCEAN DOCTORS by Juliet Shore
CRUISE NURSE by Clare Lavenham
A PROFESSIONAL SECRET by Kate Norway

CAPTIVE HEART

BY

HAZEL FISHER

MILLS & BOON LIMITED
London · Sydney · Toronto

First published in Great Britain 1983
by Mills & Boon Limited, 15–16 Brook's Mews,
London W1A 1DR

Australian copyright 1983
Philippine copyright 1983

ISBN 0 263 74291 1

Set in 10 on 12 pt Linotron Times
03/0583

Photoset by Rowland Phototypesetting Ltd
Bury St Edmunds, Suffolk
Made and printed in Great Britain by
Richard Clay (The Chaucer Press) Ltd
Bungay, Suffolk

CHAPTER ONE

DR JOHN KIRKLAND arrives tomorrow. Catherine Grainger's hands shook a little as she read the invitation for the umpteenth time. The words blurred and ran into one another. She could not see properly because of the fine mist before her eyes, then she realised she was crying, tear after tear making their way down her smooth cheeks.

A little get-together to welcome the new consultant. He would enjoy that, she thought bitterly. Of course, she had known for a few days that Dr Kirkland was coming, had made enquiries, keen to know if he was *the* Johnnie Kirkland she remembered. He was. Seeing the invitation, though, brought him nearer, conjured up his presence.

Cathy closed her smarting eyes, shutting out the drabness of the small Nursing Officer's room, the muted noise of the busy District General Hospital. She pictured the new consultant clearly—tall and lean, dark as a gipsy except for the icy blue eyes. Pale eyes, watchful, assessing. He watched, he weighed you up, and if he didn't like what he saw, he never hesitated to say so, in his blunt Geordie way.

The telephone shrilled, startling her. Cathy's hazel eyes shot open, and she picked up her pencil, putting the consultant and the invitation from her mind. Or endeavouring to. Johnnie Kirkland arrives tomorrow. The living nightmare would begin then.

'Sister Grainger!'

Cathy turned, a ready smile on her lips, as she saw Sister Peggy Davies, her only close friend at the District. Peggy's bright, dark eyes laughed at her, as she came puffing up. 'I've just had an invite—to meet this Dr Kirkland! Shall you be going?'

Cathy's smile faded. She had no choice. As an acting Nursing Officer, she would have to attend. 'Yes. I suppose I must. It's nothing to get excited about, though, doctors come and go,' she pointed out to her excitable Welsh friend, as they walked quickly along the corridor, their footsteps echoing.

The District was quiet this early in the morning. The first clinic didn't start until nine-thirty on Mondays, and Cathy's office was away in the west wing, near the surgical suite for which she was temporarily responsible.

'Yes, but this Dr Kirkland—someone here knows him!' Peggy's voice eventually broke into Cathy's thoughts, and she came over cold. Surely no-one knew? No-one here could know just how close she and Johnnie Kirkland had been.

'Oh? Who knows him?' Cathy kept her voice casual, pretending no more than a polite interest in the reply.

Peggy wrinkled her broad nose in disgust. 'Leonora Adams. Who else!'

It would have to be Leonora. 'Where did she meet him?' Cathy dropped the question casually, as they paused at the entrance to Peggy's ward.

Peggy shrugged. 'I'm not sure. I didn't ask—you know how Lea is. Has to make a big production of everything.

So I didn't swallow the bait. She hinted that she knew him well, though,' she added, with a wink.

'Not another of her ex-boyfriends, surely?' Cathy forced a smile to her lips.

'Might be. She has enough of them! Said he was a tall, dark and handsome Geordie! See you!' Peggy's short, plump figure disappeared into Ward Three, and Cathy walked on numbly.

Leonora knew him. Who else did? The Bellington District General Hospital was not far from London and Dr Kirkland was, as Peggy said, a Northerner, from County Durham. He had no relatives that she knew of in the south, except his very much older sister, but his many friends would be spread all over the country— people he'd trained with, girls he'd met and dated.

One thing was for sure. Cathy Grainger was the last person he would expect—or want—to see. But once he was over the shock, he would have a field day. Her carefully built-up reputation for coolness and competence would be torn to shreds!

When he heard what the doctors called her behind her back, he would choke on his beer. Her wide mouth curved into a smile as she walked to the administration office. He would throw his dark head back and roar with laughter. That black, almost blue-black hair, glossy and gleaming with health, soft to the touch . . .

The smile faded, and she bit her lip savagely. Catherine the Cold was what they called her. If only they knew!

The morning was hectic, as Mondays always were, and even in the canteen at lunchtime Cathy could not relax. For a Nursing Officer there were always problems to be solved. She'd thought being a ward sister was difficult enough, but being partly responsible for several wards was a nightmare. She could always turn to the Senior Nursing Officer, Mrs Smith, but whenever possible she sorted out the problems without bothering her.

She had to prove herself. She was ambitious and was determined to reach the top of the nursing tree. In her life there was only work, work and more work. After the disaster of Johnnie Kirkland, there was nothing else for Cathy *except* work.

This was only her second week as acting Nursing Officer and there were eleven more weeks to go until the other Number Seven, Edna Burn, returned from sick leave. Then Cathy could return to Women's Surgical as ward sister. She . . .

'Sister Grainger! Having a late lunch?' Dr David Connor pulled out the chair opposite her and beamed across.

A big, grizzled man nearly due for retirement, Dr Connor was extremely popular and Cathy's poor heart thawed a little as she returned his smile. 'I'm lucky to get a lunch!' she said lightly. 'Monday's problems always seem more troublesome than those later in the week!'

He grunted in agreement. 'Except for Friday afternoon's problems! They're real devils.' Dr Connor took a mouthful of his steak and kidney pie and chewed it, thoughtfully. 'I think it's real meat this week! Heard about the new consultant, have you?'

Cathy nearly choked on her glass of water. She dabbed gently at her lips with the paper napkin, struggling to keep her expression and her voice neutral. 'This Dr Kirkland?'

'Mm. Comes from the North Country. Miss Adams was telling me about him.' Dr Connor made inroads into the pie but Cathy pushed her plate away, her small appetite gone completely.

'How does Leonora know so much about him?' she asked brightly, picking up her bag ready for a quick get-away.

'Don't know. I thought she said she knew him as a boy,' he replied, brow furrowed as he tried to remember.

'But she . . .' Cathy bit back the words. Leonora Adams couldn't have known him as a boy. It wasn't possible. 'If you will excuse me, Dr Connor?'

With her usual pleasant but controlled smile, she hurried from the canteen, knowing that sooner or later she would have to see Lea and find out how much she knew about Dr Kirkland. Until she *did* know, she wouldn't be able to face tomorrow.

In her office, she gave a quick glance in the mirror as she straightened the blue cap that was part of the Nursing Officer's uniform, together with a severely-cut blue suit. Anguished hazel eyes gazed back at her, a short average sort of nose, a wide mouth, determined chin. And straight honey-blonde hair, cut very short, boyishly so. In all, an unremarkable face.

Would he recognise her after so long? Five years it was since the dynamic registrar had walked out of her life. If he had changed, so, too, had she. The long, scented honey hair was no more. There were lines at the corners of her eyes and mouth that hadn't been there then. Her once curvy figure was thin and shapeless now, or she considered it to be so. At five foot three, her slight measurements were just right for the slender frame, but she thought herself thin and bony.

Catherine the Cold. No, Johnnie wouldn't recognise her straightaway. Five years ago she was a young girl, full of life and vitality. At twenty-six she was a mature woman, her character moulded by suffering.

Johnnie Kirkland would find a difference. But would he care? If he had wanted her at any time he could have searched. She hadn't disappeared completely. Mutual friends could have told him where she was. Or her parents. But he hadn't bothered. He never sent a card, even at Christmas. It was as if Cathy Grainger had never entered his life.

Now he was a consultant in general medicine. He was a good doctor, dedicated, caring. He would make an excellent consultant. The District was lucky to get his services.

Shortly it would have to dispense with the cool Miss Grainger's services, though. The hospital wasn't big enough for both of them.

Cathy had another of those inevitable committee meetings at three, but first there was a real pleasure in store for her—an informal lecture to the junior surgical nurses to be held in the dayroom on Ward Three.

Ward Three, where Peggy Davies now ruled the roost, was Cathy's own ward. There was a possibility she would return there after her stint as a Number Seven, though her friend had settled in there quite well. Whichever ward she got, it would be surgical, for that was her speciality. A deliberate choice on her part. She was thankful for that now. At least she would be able to keep out of Dr Kirkland's way. It was unlikely they would need to meet at all, except at the regular staff meetings. Then she could arrange to sit as far away from him as possible.

Brightening at the thought, Cathy smiled with genuine warmth at Ward Three's house-doctor, Annie Sims, who flashed her a surprised smile in return.

Careful, Catherine the Cold, your mask is slipping, she mused wryly.

The youngsters rose as she entered the dayroom in the company of Staff Nurse Elliott. It made her feel old, as though they were school-girls and she was the middle-aged schoolmarm.

Twenty-seven next year. Getting old. She frowned at the thought, then gently told the girls to sit down.

Seven of them today. Word must have got around that her half-hour lectures were a good way of missing ward-chores!

'I half-prepared a talk at the weekend,' she began carefully, 'but I decided it might be more helpful to talk over some of the things that bother you, as learners. Or as nursing auxiliaries,' she added, seeing Mrs Baker, the auxiliary, standing shyly by the door.

'Do come in, Mrs Baker. There's plenty of room,' Cathy invited, and Mrs Baker's face broke into a delighted smile.

The newest recruit to the surgical section was Pupil-Nurse Nettleton, a very tall, bony girl with red-gold hair and freckles, and she hesitantly raised her hand.

'Yes, Nurse Nettleton? Tell us what you think,' Cathy encouraged, keen to bring out the rather diffident girl.

'My problem is . . . is remembering all the fancy

names for operations!' she burst out, and one of the students tittered, until quelled by a glance from Cathy's clear hazel eyes.

'There's no need to remember yet, surely? This is your first ward, isn't it?'

'Yes, Sister,' the red-faced and red-haired nurse whispered.

'A nurse's prime duty is the welfare of her patients. She has to care for them, meet their needs, keep them as free from pain as possible. Learning the patients' own names is far more important than knowing what each op is called,' Cathy assured her. Turning to the others, she went on: 'Memorising a few fancy anatomical terms doesn't make a nurse. Tender loving care is more important, and I don't think Nurse Nettleton's question was at all funny. I need to know what bothers each one of you because you are the Nursing Officers or Enrolled Nurses of the future. However silly your questions may seem to you, I want to hear them. What about you, Mrs Baker?'

'Well . . . I've been on this ward a long time, Sister, as you well know, but it's the doctors that bother me sometimes,' she said hesitantly, and Cathy encouraged her to go on.

'They don't always treat patients as people, you know. Especially them young ones,' she added, and Cathy suppressed a smile.

'In what way does it bother you?' she asked, noticing that the learners were nodding in agreement.

'They breeze in, or stagger in, depending on how many hours they've been on their feet, then they examine the women, but I feel they see only the operation site. They don't see the *whole* person. They don't care about the complete woman,' Mrs Baker went on, emphatically.

'It's true, Sister!' one of the students remarked. 'They breeze in and out, do a quick write-up in the Kardex, then they're off again.'

Cathy smiled sadly, knowing only too well the pressures young doctors faced. 'I know that and I can see your point of view, as nurses. But I can also see the young doctors' point of view. Have you any idea how many hours of work they have to cram into a week?' she began, dispassionately defending doctors, without realising she did so.

'They work at top pressure for very little reward. We work unsocial hours, split duties, and so on, but it's nothing compared with the dreadful conditions under which the house-doctors work,' she said firmly, then turned startled eyes to the open door of the dayroom, as someone began to clap.

George Redford, the senior surgical consultant, sauntered in, and the learners rose awkwardly, as did Cathy, who had been sitting comfortably in an easy-chair, slim legs crossed.

'Well said, Sister!' Mr Redford, a short, silver-haired man, beamed approvingly, and Cathy felt her cheeks flaming.

It was ridiculous. She was far too old to blush. It was second nature to defend hard-working young doctors as Johnnie had once been, and she'd allowed herself to be carried away.

Then her cheeks grew hotter and she moved nervously, as the consultant ushered in another, taller figure. A tall dark and handsome man Cathy had no difficulty at all in recognising.

There were gasps and suppressed sighs from the young nurses as Dr John Kirkland smiled at them, teeth very white in his swarthy face. A real hero straight from the romantic novels, Cathy thought in disgust, as she wrenched her eyes away from that once dear face.

'Just showing Dr Kirkland around, Sister Grainger. Only a brief stop here, I'm afraid,' Mr Redford was saying and Cathy offered her hand automatically, struggling for composure. The nightmare was beginning a day earlier than expected.

'Sister Grainger is acting Number Seven for a few months, Dr Kirkland,' Mr Redford explained. 'As she's a Nursing Officer at present I suppose we should really call her *Miss* Grainger rather than Sister. Or is it Mrs? I never can remember,' he smiled questioningly at Cathy, who said quickly:

'It's Miss Grainger, sir.'

'How do you do, Miss Grainger.' Dr Kirkland's handshake was firm, the pressure of his fingers no more than one would expect from a complete stranger. His large hand with its dark hairs completely enveloped hers, and she felt momentarily faint. His pale eyes passed over her dispassionately, missing nothing yet showing not a flicker of interest, or recognition.

The meeting she had dreaded passed off without incident. Dr Kirkland did not, it seemed, recognise her or her name.

After they went she had difficulty in composing her thoughts, but managed somehow. She sensed the girls were not as attentive as they were before. They wanted to be left alone, to discuss the handsome new consultant, to wonder aloud if he was married, to speculate about his love-life. Knowing too well the fatal appeal his dynamic looks had for women, Cathy couldn't blame them. Once she, too, had been a victim.

The afternoon passed without Cathy being aware of it doing so. As always she made Ward Three her last call after the meeting. She was supposed to finish at five but frequently found herself working until six o'clock or even later.

Ward Three was quiet and Peggy Davies was putting on her cape as Cathy walked in.

'You should be on your way home, too!' Peggy chided. 'You work far too hard. There isn't anything special—except Mrs Fraser. I've told Staff to keep an eye on her.'

Cathy nodded. Mrs Fraser was recovering from extensive abdominal surgery and had just returned to the ward from ITU. Her condition was stable but the prognosis was poor.

Cathy liked the woman, a tall thin lady of fifty. Mrs Fraser never once complained, never whined. She accepted philosophically what could not be changed. Cathy only wished she could do the same. Accept that life had to go on, however great one's losses.

She thought she *had* accepted the loss of Johnnie Kirkland. She'd carved out a career for herself, moved away from the scene of their turbulent relationship. But seeing him again, touching him, brought all the old emotions back. All the bitterness but all the love, too. She still loved Johnnie. And the knowledge hurt.

She and Peggy gazed down at Mrs Fraser's waxen

face, their eyes troubled. The patient slept so they did not need to stick falsely cheerful smiles on their faces, speak encouraging words. As they looked on, the woman moaned softly and Peggy beckoned a nurse over and gave her whispered instructions for a pain-killing drug.

Even in sleep or light unconsciousness they felt pain. Cathy's heart softened, as she drew the curtains around the bed. Here she was worrying about her broken heart, when all the time the women around her were suffering actual physical pain. She felt ashamed of her own weakness. She would survive but Mrs Fraser would not.

There was a hiss from one of the other patients and Cathy spun round, startled. Mrs Knight, a pretty blonde girl, whispered: 'How is she? The poor dear keeps moaning, but no-one has been near, Sister!'

Cathy's lips tightened, her eyes darkening until they appeared more brown than hazel. 'She's in pain but holding her own,' she whispered back, with a reassuring smile, and Mrs Knight lay back, satisfied.

How these women worried about one another! That was one of the good things about nursing. The patients watched out for others more poorly than themselves. They helped with the teas, handed out papers, lent magazines and books, had a friendly gossip. Cathy's heart warmed to them, their friendliness and comradeship making her own life, her own burdens, a little lighter.

She had a few choice words to say to Peggy about the neglect of Mrs Fraser, though, and her friend flushed. 'It's Staff Nurse's responsibility as I'm officially off-duty, Cathy. I'm sure she will have seconded someone to keep an eye on the woman.' Poor Peggy looked embarrassed and Cathy knew why. Staff Nurse Elliott was a law unto herself. Peggy was, she knew, more than a little in awe of the tall Staff Nurse, who came into nursing loaded with university degrees.

Sandra Elliott was brilliant, but understandably bitter that she'd been unable to get into medical school, despite being a doctor's daughter. Instead, she'd gone on to university then trained as a nurse at one of the top London teaching hospitals. Quite why she had moved to the smaller District hospital no-one knew. A broken romance, Cathy suspected. Whatever the reason, she was an efficient nurse but would have been better employed in a laboratory. Patients were clinical specimens to her and Cathy had more than one clash with her when she ran Ward Three.

However, speaking to her now was Peggy's responsibility and, after promising her friend full support, Cathy walked briskly away, after being assured that a second-year student would keep a watchful eye on Mrs Fraser.

Cathy had a flatlet in the Nurses' Home Annexe, where trained staff lived. Sisters and above had flatlets, SENs and Staff Nurses had only one room, but all could use the big kitchen and communal living-room. Male staff, too, lived in the Annexe, though most were married and lived out.

Cathy's flatlet had no sitting-room and only the tiniest of kitchens plus a bathroom and bedroom. The bedroom was no bigger than the bathroom, and held only a single divan, an armchair and a built-in wardrobe fitment. The chest and dressing-table were in the narrow passage between the bedroom and the bathroom. It was poky, uncomfortable and not at all what she was used to, but she lived there because it was convenient. She had no travelling problems, no housework to speak of, and it suited her just fine.

The flatlet held no photographs, no ornaments, only one mirror. It was cold and impersonal and revealed nothing of Cathy's personality, gave nothing away to prying eyes. Her parents' home, in Sussex, was breathtakingly beautiful by comparison, a ten-bedroomed mansion nestling at the foot of the South Downs.

With a sigh of exasperation because she was dwelling on the past, Cathy sank into the only armchair, kicking off her sensible nursing shoes, and closed her eyes.

A smiling Johnnie Kirkland swam before her eyes and hastily she opened them again, her anger and torment making her feel sick. How she hated him! Whoever said love and hate were akin was right, at least in her case. She both loved *and* hated him! Why couldn't he leave her alone?

The anger died. He *had* left her alone, for five long, lonely years. It was pure coincidence that he should turn up now. He wasn't following her. It was simply an ill-wind that had blown him onto the same course as herself. Even if he recognised her he wouldn't want to know. Yet he must recognise her. Five years was nothing. Why hadn't he reacted? Probably because he was as distressed and embarrassed as she was. She ought to reassure him, stress that she was prepared to put the past behind her, pretend that he was a complete stranger. Forget that they had once meant everything to each other . . .

Her face clouded, as she struggled out of her uniform

suit. Everything. They belonged to each other in the fullest possible sense of the word. Johnnie was an excellent lover, though passionate and demanding. At first he was tender, making allowances for her inexperience, her sensitive nature. Then the real Johnnie Kirkland had emerged—the darkly passionate gipsy side of his nature.

She coloured at memory of his love-making. She hugged herself, believing she could again feel those strong, muscular arms about her, hear the thudding of his heartbeat, see those beautiful blue eyes light up with love . . .

Only it wasn't love with him. She had loved him, still loved him, and he didn't care. Had never cared. She was simply a willing and foolish young woman whose body he had used. His only love was for his career. Perhaps he thought he owed her something, for her family had all but adopted him, her father paying Johnnie's way through a good school then supporting him at medical school.

Cathy had loved Johnnie even then, when he was a tall, sullen schoolboy. Maybe he felt obliged to love her, that it was expected of him, his empty words a reward for dreary little Cathy, who had followed him everywhere, her hazel eyes dumbly begging for a few crumbs of comfort.

He could not repay her parents so he had repaid her, by pretending she was the answer to his dreams, the love of his life. Cathy felt sick. She had been used and discarded. There was no point in seeking fancy names for what occurred.

Did he have a regular girl-friend? she wondered, thinking of Leonora Adams, who was a physiotherapy assistant. Tall, and blonde and tanned, with a sexual appetite which matched Johnnie's, Cathy didn't doubt.

Just how well *did* Leonora know him?

That was a question Cathy burned to ask, but for tonight it must wait.

CHAPTER TWO

CATHY was late for the reception to welcome Dr Kirkland and she heard the swell of voices as she neared the large hall where functions of this kind were held.

He was already there. Her eyes picked him out immediately as he bent his dark head to Mr Redford's level. Then Johnnie laughed, and Cathy flinched away from the sound, over-sensitive to noise today.

The morning had been a busy one which included the death of poor Mrs Fraser. Though she wasn't expected to survive for long, no-one thought she would die in hospital. She ought not to have gone so soon after the operation but it was for the best. All the same, Cathy felt sad about it, knowing how bravely the woman had borne the pain. That the death meant a lot of extra administrative work was irrelevant, but other matters had to be pushed to one side to make up for it and Cathy was hot, tired and distressed when she finally arrived. The sight and sound of Johnnie Kirkland enjoying himself was the last straw, and she snapped at Peggy before she could help herself.

Peggy's dark eyes clouded, and Cathy put a consoling hand on her shoulder. After all, Mrs Fraser was her friend's patient and she, too, had been rushed off her feet. 'Peggy, I'm so sorry,' Cathy whispered, as the crowd pushed them nearer to the new consultant. 'I've had a busy morning but that's no excuse,' she hurried on, but Peggy merely shrugged and turned away, and Cathy felt worse.

Leonora Adams, looking fresh and wide-awake in her smart uniform, peered round at sound of Cathy's voice and flashed both women an insincere smile.

Swallowing her unwarranted dislike of the woman, Cathy returned the smile, then nodded towards the new doctor, 'I hear that you're a friend of our new man, Lea! How did that come about?' Cathy kept her voice friendly but impersonal, then waited breathlessly for the reply.

Lea looked pleased. 'You aren't a one for gossip, Cathy! I'm surprised that you're interested!' she teased, then bent her head confidentially. 'Actually, I've known him for quite some time. He and I . . . Oh! Excuse me! I'll be back later.'

Cathy turned, frustrated. Lea's chief was signalling from the doorway and the tall blonde glided from sight. Now what exactly did Lea mean to say when she began 'He and I'? Was she about to say they were engaged? Or were old friends? Or . . .

Words went round and round in Cathy's head until she thought it would split. She must find out how well Lea knew him. She must.

But the crowd pushed Cathy nearer to Dr Kirkland long before Lea returned, and he gave her an impersonal smile. 'Ah, Miss Grainger, isn't it?'

'Yes, Doctor,' Cathy murmured nervously, avoiding his eyes in case she saw a flash of recognition there. In case he gazed into her large hazel eyes and remembered . . . But for some reason he did not want to remember. That knowledge, which should have pleased her, did not do so.

'I hope you enjoy your stay, Dr Kirkland,' Cathy said quietly, then moved away, seeing one or two nurses she knew well.

But his voice stopped her in mid-flight. It was low and husky and carried only to her: 'I intend to enjoy my stay, Miss Grainger. I intend to extract every ounce of enjoyment from it.'

Cathy flushed, glad her back was towards him. He knew! Of course he did. How could he not remember Cathy Grainger? He meant to play with her, make her suffer, watch her flinch. Then . . . Then what? Did he intend making love to her?

No-one but Johnnie ever had. She was his and would always remain so. Determined not to succumb without a fight, Cathy stuck out her jaw. She would show him how much little Catherine Grainger had changed!

When Lea at last reappeared, Cathy couldn't reach her before she glided up to Johnnie and smiled into his eyes. Sickened, Cathy had to watch them because she was unable to tear her eyes away. Once she, too, had gazed into those same cold, pale eyes, begging him to bestow a smile upon her.

Lea was basking in the full warmth of his personality, she saw, then young Sister Manners joined the couple, and Cathy gasped as the consultant deliberately turned towards the beautiful red-haired Amy Manners and smiled into her eyes, leaving Lea with a drink in her hand and a bitter half-smile pinned to her full lips.

At that moment Cathy felt sorry for Lea. She, too, knew what it was to enjoy Johnnie's regard one minute, then be left out in the cold the next, as someone more desirable glided into the view of his predatory eyes.

Johnnie Kirkland was a womaniser. He used then discarded them, without thought for their bruised emotions. Or their bruised bodies, either, Cathy reflected angrily, recalling incidents she had thought safely buried in the past.

He was worthless. And she had no idea why she still loved him. But she did. She only knew that she would still follow him to the ends of the earth and beyond, if he beckoned. But he would not. He wanted only to drag her down into the mire. For some reason he wanted to make her pay. Yet hadn't she paid enough? She looked five years older but he did not. There were, she noticed, traces of silvery-grey at his temples, but they merely enhanced his good looks. Time had dealt kindly with Johnnie Kirkland. Of the suffering he had caused Cathy, there was no sign. Only Cathy bore the emotional scars, and it strengthened her resolve to have nothing to do with him. Johnnie Kirkland was the past. She must look to the future. Greg Abbott *was* the future. If he didn't mind a girl-friend who was still in love with a man she hadn't seen for five years, there was some hope for their future together.

No, Johnnie Kirkland, she thought stubbornly, you won't have everything your own way this time!

She dressed carefully that evening for her date with Greg. Normally she did not accept invitations from men. Normally none of them could get close enough even to issue an invitation, she thought wryly. Catherine the Cold wasn't a recent nickname. It was one she'd acquired very soon after joining the District as a Staff Nurse. Men were kept very much at bay. Cathy simply did not want to know. But Greg, one of the senior

administrative staff, persevered. She could not explain
to him why she refused invitations, yet he seemed to
understand, seeking no more from her than she was
prepared to give. Yet this was the first time she'd agreed
to have dinner with him. In three years they had lunched
together occasionally in the staff canteen, but the times
they had lunched out Cathy could count on the fingers of
one hand.

Once, Greg took her on the river, but she felt it was
unfair to let him waste time and money on her. Evening
engagements were definitely out, she had decided. An
intimate dinner with soft lights, wine and sweet music
was an open invitation to any man and Greg was far too
sweet for her to lead him on in that way.

She didn't know why she'd changed her mind. Except
that it was a balmy summer evening and the restaurant
he'd chosen wasn't far away. The atmosphere there was
friendly and cheerful, rather than romantic, and Cathy
was determined to drink only Perrier water. It would be
fun and she only hoped Greg read nothing unusual into
her acceptance. She knew only too well how painful a
broken heart could be.

Greg always called for her, knocking on her flatlet
door, then courteously waiting downstairs near the communal sitting-room. He guessed she would feel press-
urised if he asked to wait in her tiny kitchen, with the
bedroom only inches away.

His knock came, loud and confident, so unlike the
man himself, and Cathy smiled a little as she surveyed
herself in the bathroom mirror. Her dress was gold and
green taffeta with a full skirt and modest bodice. Her
only jewellery was the gold locket Johnnie had given her

once, and which she always wore off-duty. It brought him nearer.

Angry with herself for even *wanting* him nearer, she opened the door and greeted the bearded Greg Abbott.

His smile warmed her, as always, his deep-set grey eyes lighting up, showing his appreciation of her. Those eyes flicked over her now in admiration and Cathy wouldn't have been a woman if she hadn't welcomed his admiration, basked in the warmth of his smile. She was ready so he didn't need to wait, and Cathy still glowed inwardly as they walked downstairs towards the main entrance.

Then the glow turned to ashes as the tall, dark man moved out of the shadows to intercept them. White teeth gleamed in the dark-complexioned face, and Cathy swallowed, nervously. Was this to be a confrontation? Did he intend showing her up here?

'Why, it's Miss Grainger! I'd no idea you lived here!' Johnnie seemed genuinely surprised, but Cathy didn't believe him. He knew all right, but she didn't know that he had moved into the Annexe.

Of course she had no option but to introduce them, forgetting that they must already have met at the reception.

'I've met Mr Abbott, thank you,' Johnnie said affably as the men shook hands. 'I'll not keep you. Off to paint the town red, I suppose?' he went on, his smile chilling or seeming so to Cathy's over-worked imagination.

To her annoyance, Greg told him where they were going, and she half-expected Johnnie to follow them there. Or even ask if he might tag along, but he did not.

He intended she should squirm a bit longer, she thought, coldly furious as Greg drove to the restaurant.

Now he knew about Greg the pressure would be on. Johnnie Kirkland would take his pound of flesh—and more.

'Seems a pleasant chap. Cold eyes, though,' Greg murmured, and she shot him a suspicious glance. He turned innocent grey eyes on her and smiled, and she sank back, satisfied that he hadn't guessed.

She must be so careful. No hint of scandal must touch her name. She must not show by word or glance that she and Dr Kirkland were very well acquainted.

A sigh escaped her, and Greg chuckled as they drew into the car-park of the riverside restaurant. Yet he made no comment until they were seated at a table in the middle of the dining-room, which he had booked specially, knowing she would not care for some dark, intimate corner.

Realising this, she smiled warmly at him as the waiter glided away with their order. 'Thank you for bringing me here, Greg. I . . . I *do* appreciate it.' She leaned forward, hazel eyes anxious. He was a lovely man and she could give him so little. And it hurt.

He shrugged. 'It's little enough after all you have done for me.'

She frowned, not understanding. 'I can't remember doing a lot for you!' she said lightly.

'Oh, but you have, Cathy,' he insisted, giving her slim hand a friendly pat. 'I haven't enjoyed myself so much for years. Not since Mary died.'

Cathy felt uncomfortable. Greg was a widower and was in his late forties or early fifties, she judged. He had

been a widower for less than a year when Cathy arrived
at the District and he evidently found her undemanding
friendship helpful in overcoming his loss, just as she
found his helpful. Yet she didn't want to raise his hopes,
lead him to believe that their friendship could go on *ad
infinitum*. It simply wasn't fair. And now that Johnnie
had turned up, it simply wasn't possible. Once the full
story came out, she would have to leave. She couldn't
bear to stay on.

'How . . . how is your daughter?' Cathy broke what to
her was an awkward silence, and he grimaced.

'She's simply being Emma!' he joked. 'Wants to be an
actress now.'

'Does she? What happened to her nursing ambitions?'
Cathy was surprised. Emma, Greg's seventeen-year-
old daughter, had seemed determined on a nursing career.

'That idea came about because Irene, my daughter-in-
law, had that long spell in hospital. The idea of becoming
an actress was put into Emma's head because she did
well at some amateur theatrical class!' He sounded
amused, a typical indulgent father, and Cathy laughed.

'The apple of your eye, is she?'

'A father always feels closer to a daughter than he
does to a son, you know. You must meet Emma,' he
went on, and Cathy mentally baulked. 'Encourage her,
tell her about the dedication needed to nurse the sick,'
he continued blandly, and Cathy relaxed.

It was an impersonal suggestion, after all. He wasn't
suggesting she meet Emma to be looked over as a
possible stepmother!

'He's the one, isn't he?' Greg went on perceptively,

and Cathy flinched, as though struck, understanding him only too well.

Painfully, she nodded, then the main course was placed before them and she pushed away her untouched fruit juice. 'Yes,' she whispered, averting her eyes. 'He's the one.'

'Dangerous sort of chap, I should think. Wouldn't want to get on the wrong side of him,' Greg said mildly, and she shot him a puzzled glance.

Then she realised what he meant. He did not intend to fight Johnnie for her, did not want to risk the consultant's displeasure. 'Don't worry, he won't bite!' she laughed, but it was an empty sound. 'I won't let him dissect you!' she went on, but Greg shook his head, irritably.

'No, no, Cathy. You misunderstood me. I think you are *worth* fighting for. But I have to know—is there any hope for me if I can exorcise this other man's spell?' Again he patted her hand, squeezing her fingers gently. 'Come on, eat up. Mustn't waste good food!' he joked, when she could not bring herself to reply to his question.

Although her appetite had gone, Cathy made an effort to eat most of the food, succulent steak with french fries and broccoli, her favourite vegetable.

Greg appeared to have no trouble finishing his and she envied him his apparent unconcern. Here she was with her whole world about to tumble about her ears and he was tucking into his steak as though he hadn't a care in the world.

Men! She wasn't sure she liked men, not after Johnnie Kirkland's abrasive company, but she couldn't help the soft spot she had for Greg. He was a good man and deserved more than she could provide.

When the pudding, a mousse, was placed before them, she answered his question: 'No, Greg. There isn't any hope for you. One day you will understand why,' she said huskily.

He bore the news stoically. 'I half expected you to say that. Dr Kirkland must be really something! One hell of a man!'

Cathy swallowed. She couldn't find the right words to describe Johnny or her feelings for him, so she agreed that he was one hell of a man and left it at that. He had certainly dragged *her* through hell!

They were back at the Nurses' Home Annexe soon after ten. Neither of them wanted to prolong the evening. Cathy simply wanted to relax in a hot bath and have an early night. No doubt she would dream of the darkly handsome Johnnie Kirkland, she reflected ruefully. There would not be much sleep for her.

But she did sleep. The bath relaxed her, as did the mugful of Ovaltine she permitted herself, and she drifted into a dreamless sleep, wakening early.

For a moment she couldn't remember what day it was. Wednesday. Was there something special about Wednesday? she wondered, then she knew. It was the day of the weekly staff meeting, the day Dr Kirkland would be settling down to his new routine. He would certainly wish to attend the meeting. It would give him a chance to meet his colleagues in a more business-like setting than yesterday's reception.

Would he speak to her? Make some move? Tell everyone how well he knew Catherine the Cold?

Cathy was sitting at the kitchen table when there was a tap at her door. As she was still in her nightie and housecoat she was reluctant to answer. Then it came again, and she glanced irritably at the clock. Not yet six-thirty. It might be urgent.

Fastening the sash of the vivid green housecoat, she opened the door a crack. Then tried to close it again, panic seizing her, but the crack widened as Johnnie Kirkland wedged his foot in it and Cathy's weight wasn't enough to close the door in his face.

He edged in, smiling affably, and Cathy backed away before she regained her courage and stood her ground. Carefully, Johnnie shut and locked the door and turned back to her, still smiling, a wolfish smile which did not reach the cold, watchful blue eyes.

'Expecting company, were you?' he enquired, his expert gaze stripping away the garments she wore, seeing right through them to the slender body beneath.

Cathy flushed under his caressing eyes, then said mutinously: 'Whatever you want, the answer is no! Please get out of my flat! I . . . I never want to see you again,' she added, almost believing it herself.

'What a welcome! And to think I was once the love of your life! Your love didn't last long, Miss Grainger,' he taunted.

'Neither did yours,' she said tartly, before recalling that he had never loved her, never once spoken of love.

He shrugged, his gaze missing no detail of the poky kitchen. 'Hardly a palace, is it? What's through here?' Before she could stop him he'd passed through to the equally tiny bedroom, and she was thankful she'd made the bed and not left it open to air as she generally did.

'Neat and tidy as ever,' he commented, his husky voice dripping with sarcasm, and Cathy bit back the retort that sprang to her lips. There was no point in quarrelling with him.

He wandered through to the bathroom, then back to where she stood by the kitchen sink, her back to the window, muscles tensed to fight him off if he made any move towards her.

He didn't look as if he'd just got out of bed. He was dressed for the day's work in a dark grey suit, the jacket unbuttoned showing the elegant waistcoat, crisp pale blue shirt, subdued tie. Every inch the successful consultant, she thought bitterly. And it was her parents' money that helped put him there.

He perched on a corner of the kitchen table, feet firmly on the lino-covered floor. Involuntarily, her eyes went to his legs, those long muscular legs now so elegantly clad. Long legs that, years before, had entwined with hers, keeping her pinned to the bed when she'd wanted to escape his advances.

She couldn't prevent the hot sweep of colour, and Johnnie chuckled. He didn't miss a thing! And she hated him all the more.

'Wishing we could get together again, are you?' he asked innocently, and she shook her head in quick denial, unable to meet his gaze.

When he sprang off the table she cowered back, pressing herself against the sink, and he chuckled again. He was now only inches from her, yet made no move to touch her.

'Tense, aren't you? Did you think I was going to assault you?' he enquired, pleasantly enough, but she wasn't deceived by his apparent good humour.

'Tell me what you want and then go!' she snapped, her patience at an end. She forced herself to meet his pale eyes, and saw the mocking amusement there.

'I came to say hello, Miss Grainger,' he assured her. 'Nothing more. I knew you would be up. Always the little lark, weren't you?'

'Yes, yes, I suppose I was. I was the lark and you were the night-owl,' she said, suddenly recalling his liking for sleeping late. It was funny how little things like that were so soon forgotten. He'd never been an early riser. It was she who had to shake him awake, sometimes flicking his face with cold water before he would budge!

'I see you *do* remember,' he went on softly, and she closed her eyes with the pain of remembering.

When she flicked them open again, he was smiling to himself as if he, too, was lost in the past.

'Do . . . do you intend mentioning our . . . relationship?' she asked, reluctantly, thinking more of Leonora than of the rest of the hospital. He might well be serious about her, might even intend marrying her.

'Relationship? Was that what it was? I might—given provocation,' he warned, his eyes cold again. 'Get rid of that bearded chap.'

'Greg? But he's only a friend!' she protested.

'How good a friend?' he asked silkily, his gaze holding hers.

She shook her head, willing him to understand. 'He isn't *that* sort of friend! We . . . we've never . . . I mean he isn't my lover!' She forced the words out, embarrassed at having to spell it out for him.

'You're sure?'

She nodded, and he seemed to relax. 'There's no problem then. I don't want you and you don't want me.'

Something within her died at his words but she kept her expression bland. 'That's it.'

'But if I *do* decide to pick up our *relationship* where we left off, I don't want to fall over any rivals,' he warned baring his teeth in what she supposed was a smile.

Angrily she tossed her head. 'Well, I don't want to pick up where we left off! So you needn't bother to hang around, Dr Kirkland!' she flung at him.

'That's all right then,' he said agreeably enough, and Cathy wanted to bite back her words. She wanted him yet did not. She knew she had no intention of renewing their love affair, and yet . . .

He sighed, then glanced at the gold wrist-watch on his muscular wrist. She saw, with a pang, that it wasn't the one she had given him. That was on an expensive leather strap. This one had an expanding bracelet, and she wondered if it was a gift from one of her many successors.

'Time to go, I suppose. A quick bite to eat, then catch them unawares on the ward!' he chuckled.

'You're up early—for a night-owl,' she observed shakily, glad to see him go yet curiously disappointed that he'd made no play for her.

He smiled, the lines between his nose and mouth deepening as though he was genuinely amused. 'My current girlfriend is an early riser. It's catching.'

'Oh! I'll let you out,' Cathy said coldly, wondering if Leonora was the early riser.

'Thank you,' he said affably, then pinned her against the door as she made to open it. Her face was towards the door, his chest pressing against her slender back, and tremors shot right through her body. He had no right to torment her like this! He was cruel, despicable . . .

Gently he turned her stiff, unyielding body and enfolded her in his arms. Strong arms that resisted her attempts to escape.

His mouth tasted just as good as she remembered and she had no will left to refuse him. She groaned, hating yet loving him at the same time. Then he nuzzled her ear, while her beating heart was held against his, the nearness of that hard, masculine body doing crazy things to her equilibrium.

She renewed her earlier efforts to escape, drawing a husky chuckle from Johnnie.

'You can't escape me, Miss Grainger,' he taunted, before his lips met hers in a kiss, gentle at first then increasingly demanding and flame seared through Cathy's body. When he put her from him, she felt bereft, chilled, yearning for much more than a kiss.

But a kiss, it seemed, was all she was to get for he straightened his tie, and smiled at her. 'Must get on, Miss Grainger. Sorry I can't stop for more,' he said equably, his eyes mocking her.

'You pig!' she ground out, and he raised a bushy dark brow in feigned surprise.

'Shame on you, Miss Grainger! I didn't know you used such words!' He paused, his hand on the door-key. 'I've heard what they call you here—Catherine the Cold!' he laughed. 'If you're cold, I don't know what they consider hot! See you!'

The door shut behind him and Cathy sank to the floor, her eyes tightly closed in agony.

When a drained and bone-weary Cathy went on her rounds a little later, she sensed an atmosphere on Ward Three. It was nothing she could put her finger on, and at first she believed it was her own aroused sensitivity, her imagination, nothing more.

Peggy Davies was off-duty today and Staff Nurse Elliott was in charge, to Cathy's annoyance. She particularly wanted to see Peggy, to apologise properly for her outburst of ill-humour at the reception.

Staff Nurse Elliott was efficient, though, and Cathy had no qualms about the woman being in charge. Yet when she spoke to the Staff Nurse she realised that the unhappy, tense atmosphere emanated from the nurse, not from the ward itself.

Cathy turned puzzled eyes on the Staff Nurse as she sat across the desk from her. 'Is anything the matter, Staff? No difficulties?' She smiled reassuringly, but her friendliness was rebuffed as Sandra Elliott shot her a chilling glance.

'Nothing I can't handle thank you, Sister,' she said, fiddling with the silver buckle on her navy-blue belt. Then she added, defiantly: 'If you think I can't cope, you had better get a replacement!'

Astonished, Cathy rose to her feet, the duty-sheet clasped defensively to her chest. 'I wasn't suggesting you couldn't cope, Staff Nurse! I thought you seemed worried, preoccupied,' she added gently, not sure how to get through to the proud young woman before her.

Staff Nurse flushed. 'I *am* preoccupied. This Mrs Fraser . . .' she began, then stopped.

'Yes? Go on. What about her?' Cathy prompted, believing that the girl felt guilty because she had left the woman in pain.

'Nothing.' She shook her head, then gave Cathy a triumphant look. 'Her son is coming down from Suffolk today. You will have to see him.'

Cathy frowned. 'Sister saw all the close relatives yesterday, Nurse.'

'The son couldn't get down in time. He's coming just after lunch. He telephoned earlier and I said you would see him.'

'Did you? Was that within your jurisdiction?' Cathy asked, her voice deceptively soft, and Nurse Elliott shuffled, awkwardly.

'No, but I knew you wouldn't want *me*, of all people, to see him!' she flashed.

Cathy was about to remonstrate with her when the telephone rang and automatically she reached out a hand to answer it, forgetting that it was no longer her ward.

But it was for her. Mrs Walton, the Principal Nursing Officer, wanted to see her straight away. With a cool smile for the Staff Nurse, Cathy hurried to the PNO's office, wondering what emergency had caused her to telephone.

If there was anything special a Number Seven had to be told, then it came via the Number Eight, the Senior Nursing Officer. To be summoned directly to the PNO boded ill, but Cathy could think of nothing she'd done. Then Johnnie's face floated before her as she sped along the corridor. Was it to do with him?

All her hopes, her dreams, crashed about her as she slowed her pace. That must be it. Johnnie Kirkland was extracting payment in full.

CHAPTER THREE

THE Principal Nursing Officer smiled, and Cathy relaxed a little. 'Do sit down, Sister. I've asked for some coffee.'

Cathy perched awkwardly on the edge of the hard chair which was directly in front of Mrs Walton's desk. It was a big desk, for Mrs Walton was a big woman, a buxom, motherly type. Cathy wasn't usually in awe of her, but today all her self-confidence had vanished. First there had been Johnnie, her early-morning visitor. Then the curious remark made by Staff Nurse Elliott. The prospect of seeing Mrs Fraser's son wasn't a happy one, either. There was so little one could say to bereaved relatives.

'Not feeling well today, Sister?' Mrs Walton asked, blue eyes sharp, and Cathy pulled herself together.

'I'm a bit tired, Matron. I didn't sleep well,' she lied. 'You wanted to see me about something?' she went on, anxious to get it over with.

Mrs Walton smiled. 'It will keep, Sister. Let's enjoy our coffee first. It isn't often I get the chance to relax,' she sighed, and Cathy nodded understandingly.

The District was a fair size and all the nursing problems eventually found their way to Mrs Walton's in-tray. It wasn't a job Cathy would relish, yet she was ambitious and one day she supposed she might reach the dizzy heights of Senior Nursing Officer even if she never made it any further. But was that nursing? she mused, as Mrs

Walton seemed in no hurry to talk, merely reading through her mail.

Nursing was caring for people, easing their pain, reassuring them. Nursing Officers, she felt, were doing work that could very often be done by administrative staff and sometimes would be better performed by them. All in all, she would not be sorry to return to her ward sister's post. That is, if she could stay at the District. A lot depended on Mrs Walton.

The coffee arrived and Cathy absently stirred a spoonful of brown sugar into her cup before she remembered that she'd given up sugar. That was the state she was in. She could not relax until she knew why she'd been summoned to the holy of holies.

'Settling in all right, Sister Grainger?' the PNO asked suddenly, and Cathy shot her a wary look. The PNO's expression was bland and gave nothing away.

'It's early days yet, Matron,' Cathy said, evasively. 'I miss Ward Three, though.'

'Ah, yes, Ward Three. How is Staff Nurse Elliott shaping up?'

Warning bells rang in Cathy's head as she sipped the coffee. Something was up, but what? Relieved that the interview apparently had nothing to do with Johnnie Kirkland Cathy smiled. 'She's very efficient, Matron. Well qualified.'

'Qualifications aren't everything,' Mrs Walton said dryly. 'She came to see me yesterday. Well, she saw the SNO who asked me to see her. Staff Nurse seems to think you have a down on her, are perhaps jealous of her degree.'

Cathy's head shot up in surprise. Carefully, she put

the coffee-cup down on a corner of the desk, while she sought for words. 'If she had any complaints, she ought to have brought them to me first,' she said coldly.

'She felt you would victimise her, Sister.' Mrs Walton sounded amused, which was a hopeful sign, but even so it was a serious allegation, a slur on Cathy's character.

'I lean over backwards to be helpful to her.' With an effort Cathy kept her voice down, but she wanted to scream, and thump the desk, so great was her anger. 'She has a chip on her shoulder. Staff Nurse feels she ought to have been promoted by now, but that is hardly my fault,' Cathy pointed out.

Mrs Walton tapped her pencil against her blotter, head bent in thought. 'It's no-one's fault but her own. One day, when she realises that patients are people not merely interesting collections of diseases or symptoms, we will promote her. Hopefully she will leave nursing— or marry, before that day!' Mrs Walton said fervently, and Cathy wanted to hug her.

'However,' the PNO went on, 'some remark was made, apparently to Sister Davies, about Staff Nurse's care of Mrs Fraser. It seems that it was blown up out of all proportion, but perhaps it was better left unsaid?' she suggested.

Cathy bit her lip, 'I *did* tell Peg—Sister Davies, that is, that Mrs Fraser had been left in pain when she ought to have been sedated.' She hesitated, not wanting to tell her senior that Staff Nurse Elliott had disobeyed instructions and left the patient alone. 'Perhaps my remark was unwise, but . . .' Cathy looked to the PNO for guidance.

'Tact is normally one of your strongest points, Sister. Sometimes it *is* difficult to know how to handle staff—

particularly people such as Miss Elliott. We'll say no more.'

Gratefully, Cathy picked up her cup again and drained it, sugar and all. She was trembling inwardly. Surely her criticism hadn't been out of place? Being Cathy, she would worry about her apparent short-comings for weeks to come.

Mrs Walton went so far as to see Cathy to the door, an honour indeed, and Cathy beamed at her, the worries sliding off her shoulders just for a few seconds.

'You've met our new consultant then?' The question came out of the blue and Cathy paused, halfway out of the door.

'Yes—Yes, I have, Matron.' She waited, hardly daring to breathe.

'Did you know he was coming here or was it a surprise, Sister?'

Cathy closed her eyes against the sudden pain. She had forgotten how much Mrs Walton knew. 'It was more of a shock than a surprise!' she said jerkily, wondering if she had relaxed too soon.

'He is living in the Annexe until the house he's bought is ready for occupation,' Mrs Walton said quietly, and Cathy's anguished gaze met hers.

'His private life is no concern of mine, Matron. Not any more,' she insisted, and the PNO gave a sad smile.

'See that there is no cause for gossip, Sister. You have talent as well as ambition and I know you're keen to get on.' The words were kindly but the unspoken threat was there. No nocturnal wanderings for her and Dr Kirk-land!

Shaken, Cathy hurried back to her own office, away

on the other side of the hospital. Mrs Walton knew about Johnnie, of course. She'd forgotten that. Worry and fear had driven out all coherent thoughts, had blocked her memory. She had nothing to fear from the PNO, whom everyone unthinkingly still called 'Matron'. Only if Johnnie decided to tell their colleagues would there be gossip, speculation. That would be a field day for Staff Nurse Elliott. A field day for Johnnie Kirkland, too.

In the safety of her office, Cathy struggled for control. She was still trembling, both with fear that her relationship with the handsome consultant would come to light and with anger at Staff Nurse Elliott. The supercilious young madam! She had no right to be a nurse and should never have been accepted for training, degree or no degree.

Cathy began on the mound of paperwork that seemed to accumulate whenever she left the office for a few minutes and, apart from obligatory visits to the surgical wards, she worked undisturbed until almost lunchtime.

She wasn't aware that lunch was due until she heard the timid tap on her half-open door. Looking up with a smile, she saw three students she knew slightly, one of them having worked on her own ward.

'We hope we aren't disturbing you, Sister Grainger. Are you going to lunch? If you are we can come back later,' the student she knew said quickly, then Cathy saw one of the others poke the girl in the ribs.

'I didn't know it *was* lunchtime, I've been so busy,' Cathy assured them, eyes narrowed thoughtfully. What on earth could they want?

The tallest of the three had eyes the same colour as

Johnnie and that set Cathy brooding on her problem again. So much so that she did not pay as much attention as she would have done to their request.

'So will you back us, Sister?' the tall student asked earnestly, and automatically, Cathy nodded. The girl had the same dark complexion, too. She couldn't be a relative, could she? The girl's name-badge said C. Semadini, but Cathy didn't recognise the name.

'You want me to sponsor you?' Cathy asked, having gathered that they were walking for the hospital fund, and Ann Ives, Cathy's former student, began to interrupt but was swiftly silenced by the others.

'If you please, Sister. We would all be grateful,' Nurse Semadini said humbly. Too humbly in Cathy's opinion but she wasn't going to argue with them.

'It will be in your own time?' Cathy queried and was reassured by the chorus of agreement.

With a few words of encouragement, Cathy sent them away and, because she wasn't hungry, decided to skip lunch and have a quick walk through the wards. This afternoon, before the meeting, she must see Mr Fraser, then a lecture at the school of nursing. She couldn't see herself finishing at five tonight but it was for the best. It gave her less time to brood.

'Oh, Sister! I was just going to bleep you!' SEN Young's voice cut in on Cathy's sombre thoughts as she strolled into the office on Ward Two, men's surgical.

'It's Mr Sutton, Sister. I wonder if you would mind looking at his drip,' the newly-qualified SEN asked, then hurried to the ward, without waiting for Cathy's quick nod.

'I didn't like to worry the ward doctor, and I wasn't

too sure,' SEN Young explained, and Cathy was able to reassure her that all was well.

The girl really ought to have known that herself. If she had looked properly she would have seen that the infusion wasn't leaking into the tissues, and Cathy pointed this out gently, making sure the nurse knew she wasn't to blame but making her aware that a little more thought would be a good idea sometimes.

'If you have any more problems, Nurse Young, let me know and I'll help you solve them yourself,' Cathy finished, leaving the relieved SEN.

Ward Three ought to be visited again but they would be in the thick of lunches now and wouldn't appreciate a visit from a Nursing Officer. Cathy hesitated, torn two ways, knowing that she didn't want to go on Ward Three. She had her bleep if anything untoward happened, anyway. Her conscience assuaged, Cathy decided to make the children's ward her next visit, keeping Ward Three to the very last.

'Hello, Cathy!' Leonora's bright voice and face came into view, reminding Cathy of their unfinished conversation. She waited until the physio assistant caught up with her, wondering how she might steer the conversation towards the subject of Dr Kirkland.

They chatted about hospital matters as they strolled towards the main entrance. It wasn't where Cathy had intended going but she wasn't going to leave Lea! She could, in any case, check her mail while she was there.

Lea still chattered on gaily while Cathy enquired for mail at the hall porter's desk. There was none, not even from her parents. Probably they were away.

It wasn't until they really had to go their separate ways

that Lea mentioned the person uppermost in Cathy's mind. 'I'm off-duty this afternoon so I'm going to do my Good Samaritan act,' Lea confided as Cathy paused outside the children's ward.

'Oh? Helping at a fête somewhere?' Cathy asked, her mind already on the problems she might meet on the ward.

'No! Good heavens! I'm not *that* good, Cathy dear!' Lea laughed, the noise grating on Cathy's nerves. 'I'm helping Dr Kirkland to choose furniture for his new home. He's buying a house at Cross Square. Do you know it?'

The area she named was an exclusive part of Bellington, with big houses, modern yet full of character, and Cathy nodded. 'Why has he asked you? Hasn't he got a wife?' Her voice shook a little, but Lea was too wrapped up in herself to notice.

She smiled archly. 'I'm trying to make myself indispensible to the dashing doctor!' Lea laughed. 'He's at some meeting this afternoon, so I'll go window-shopping, see if anything takes my fancy. He has implicit trust in my judgment,' she added, and Cathy went cold.

Once he'd had implicit faith in *her* judgment, but that was water under the bridge now.

'He's a lovely person. Very sexy.' Lea lowered her voice confidentially, and Cathy tried to look interested. 'Personally, I don't think he's the marrying kind, but there is no harm in hoping!'

Lea's words stayed with Cathy as she finished her rounds. I don't think he is the marrying kind. Lea was quite right. Dr Kirkland wasn't the marrying kind. He ought not to be tied down. He must be free, free as the gipsies to whom her mother had suspected he was related.

Johnnie was an orphan, a transplanted Geordie living in Sussex, when Cathy and her family met him. He was a tall, very thin boy with a shock of black hair, and a wild look in those light eyes. He lived with his much older sister and her family but did not fit in. The sister saw that Johnnie never went short of anything but she was a widow and there was no man in the house to discipline the boy. Johnnie was short of love even if he never went without material things, and Cathy's soft heart had melted at the look of misery she saw in his eyes sometimes, before he put up the shutters and became distant, untouchable.

Cathy followed him everywhere, like a shadow, a very small shadow, but he had never complained, never turned on her irritably, the way her own brother did. He was patient with the nine-years-younger Cathy, and treated her like a kid sister.

Eventually his sister found she could no longer cope with the often sullen, always independent-minded boy, and Cathy's parents took him in, more for Cathy's sake than for his own, she realised now.

With her he was a different person and some of her most treasured memories were those of their childhood—Johnnie setting off in style to his new boarding-school, where he eventually rose to be Head Boy; Johnnie going to medical school; and best of all, Johnnie, newly-qualified, kissing her after a dinner to celebrate.

Cathy's lips moved but no sound came. Oh Johnnie, I love you! she cried silently, making her way back to her office where she'd been told Mr Fraser was waiting. If I loved you then, I love you ten times as much now! Seeing him again, feeling the touch of his lips proved that beyond doubt. If only there was some way she could take back the heated words, undo the past, right the many wrongs she felt she'd done him. But Lea was helping him furnish his new house and he said he had a new girl-friend. He didn't need little Cathy Grainger any more.

He had made use of her, taken everything she had to offer including her heart, taken all he could from her family as well. Now he didn't want to know them. The man wasn't worth loving! she thought crossly, but she could no more help loving Johnnie than breathing. Now it was too late.

The afternoon was less traumatic than Cathy had feared and she was home by five-thirty. Home to a flatlet and a lonely evening with a novel or a nursing magazine. The prospect wasn't inviting and on the spur of the moment she decided to call on Peggy Davies. Peggy would be off tomorrow as well, Cathy saw from the duty-sheet, and she really ought to make up in some way for her sharp retort the previous day. Although she and Peggy weren't *that* close, they sometimes went to the theatre together or had a meal out, and Cathy in fact had tickets for a new production for the following week. Tickets that a ward sister had sold because her husband was ill and couldn't go. Peggy would enjoy the play.

Cathy was almost at Peggy's house when she realised how near she was to Cross Square. Why, Peggy lived almost on Johnnie's doorstep! She slowed her Mini, fighting the desire to see where he lived. Curiosity won and she chuckled as she turned into Cross Square. She didn't even know which house he'd bought, but there was no harm in looking.

Cross Square was part of a huge estate, but that was the last word one would use to describe the area. Each house or bungalow was architect-designed, each different, some with three bedrooms, some with more. Cathy knew the architect concerned, and had seen the plans for herself. There were plenty of trees, now in full leaf. It was restful, tranquil, and Cathy felt some of the tension easing as she drove slowly around, trying to pinpoint a house that looked empty. Probably there would be curtains at the window, though.

An estate-agent's board caught her eyes as she came nearly to the end. It was a 'Sold' board and stood against the low brick wall of an imposing house with a large front garden and double garage. From the design Cathy decided it was one of the four-bedders and she wondered why he needed such a big house. He had no children, after all. A knife twisted inside her and she hurriedly shut out the thought.

Once, he nearly had a child, but he never knew. The baby she'd been carrying when he walked out had miscarried for no apparent reason. Nature's way of getting rid of impure stock, she reflected bitterly, stopping the car for a closer look at Johnnie's house. He never knew and even if he had, he wouldn't have cared. Oh, he would have come back, done his duty, stayed by her side. She knew that, knew also that she didn't want that. He was a proud, untamed animal and she'd had no right to cage him. They should never have . . .

Resolutely, she shut out the past, slipped the Mini into reverse and turned easily in the Square.

As she rang Peggy's doorbell, Cathy rehearsed what she ought to say. Peg was a dear but so sensitive. She was, Cathy knew, concerned that Cathy would get Ward Three back when her stint as a Number Seven was over, and there was no way she could reassure her friend about that. When the time came she must take whichever ward was offered. At least it would not be a medical one, thank goodness. Imagine the trauma of seeing Dr Kirkland twice a week!

The smile died on her lips as the subject of her thoughts answered the doorbell, Peggy by his side.

There was a short, uncomfortable silence, then Peggy laughed and drew Cathy inside. 'Dr Kirkland was just going, even though I begged him to stay for coffee. You must both have some now.'

Peggy bustled away and Cathy had no option but to follow, Johnnie courteously making her a little half-bow as she preceded him. She felt hot and uncomfortable, wishing she'd worn something prettier for him. The elegant linen suit of tiny blue stripes was servicable but not the kind of outfit he liked her to wear.

Then she shook herself. She didn't know why she was bothering. He wasn't the slightest bit interested in what she wore, but old habits died hard.

She wondered what he was doing at Peggy's, but her friend explained that she'd persuaded the doctor to join the committee of one of the many charitable ventures in which she was interested. This one was concerned with children and Cathy sighed involuntarily. How she loved children, yet she felt Johnnie did not and wondered why Peggy should bother him about it.

Cathy sipped her coffee, painfully aware of Johnnie's long, muscular legs so near her own. Peggy's sitting-room was huge, a through room with views to rear garden as well as the front. From where she sat, Cathy could look out into the rear garden, watch the apple trees sway in the wind. It gave her something to do. Anything was better than talking to Johnnie.

Of course she made polite conversation with him. That much she could manage without tears, but she was mightily relieved when he replaced his cup on the coffee-table and stretched, yawning a little.

Of their own volition her eyes followed the move-ment. He was casually dressed in brown cords, a light shirt and what appeared to be a hand-knitted pullover. Which of his many women had knitted that, she won-dered bleakly, then he caught her staring. Face flushed, she bent her head, toying with the spoon in her cup, wishing Johnnie Kirkland a thousand miles away.

He smiled pleasantly at them both, only Cathy was aware that the smile did not reach those cold, penetrat-ing eyes. She was about to make some non-committal comment to relieve her own tension, when Peggy asked her why she'd come.

'Was it something special, like?' her friend queried. Since she could not apologise in front of Johnnie, Cathy had to mention the theatre tickets. Unfortunately, it proved to be a night Peggy was heavily committed to charitable work but she made the bright suggestion that perhaps Dr Kirkland might be free to accompany Cathy.

The colour left Cathy's face, and she went cold all

over. What a suggestion! Exquisite torture, if Peggy did but know.

'I'm sure Dr Kirkland has many other commitments, Peggy,' Cathy said sweetly. 'But if you could use *both* the tickets you're very welcome to them,' she added, turning to Johnnie.

His smile deepened and he seemed highly amused, though only Cathy knew why. 'I should be honoured to accompany you to the theatre, Sister Grainger,' he said formally, and Peggy smiled at them both.

'That's settled then. Do you good to get out, it will,' she told Cathy, who flinched, wondering what secrets her friend was about to divulge. 'But you mustn't be so formal!' Peggy went on. 'Dr Kirkland is Johnnie and Sister Grainger is Cathy.' She performed the introductions and this time the smile *did* reach Johnnie's eyes.

Cathy burned with embarrassment. She needed no introduction to the dashing Dr Kirkland!

After making a note of the theatre-date in his diary, Johnnie left, and Cathy sank wearily onto the old pouffe in front of the unlit fire. Somehow, some way, she must get out of the theatre visit, but how? How? She ran long, slender fingers through her short hair, distraught but trying not to show it.

'Is something the matter?' Peggy queried, her happy smile fading once the doctor had gone.

Cathy raised her head, trying to pull herself together. Hesitantly, she apologised for her hasty remark of the previous day—a remark Peggy appeared to have forgotten already.

'Not to worry, Cathy! Had a hard day, have you? How is Ward Three?' Peggy went on casually.

'I saw Mrs Fraser's son. He was most appreciative of the care his mother received at the District.' Cathy wondered if she ought to tell Peggy about the Staff Nurse Elliott affair and decided she ought to. Ward Three was Peggy's ward, after all.

Her friend shrugged after she'd heard Cathy out. 'You know Staff Nurse Elliott. Has a chip on her shoulder as big as a dinner-plate! You *worry* too much, Cathy.'

They parted good friends again, though Cathy refused Peggy's invitation to supper. She just wanted to hurry back to her poky flat and work out ways and means of escaping her date with Dr Kirkland.

With a sigh of relief Cathy let herself into the flatlet, leaving the door open while she switched on the light and drew the curtains. When she turned back, Johnnie Kirkland was in the process of closing the door and she gasped, the more so when he locked it as well.

'Had a good evening?' he asked pleasantly, seating himself at the kitchen table.

Cathy sought for words but could only manage a strangled shriek.

He raised a dark brow sardonically. 'If that strange noise meant do I want a cup of coffee, the answer is yes,' he said, his eyes crinkling at the corners as he smiled.

Warily, Cathy prepared the coffee, not sure of his motive. 'I thought you had enough coffee at Peggy's,' she said hesitantly, and he smiled even more. It was a cat-who-got-the-cream smile and boded ill for Cathy.

He said no more until she placed the steaming mug of coffee before him. 'No biscuit?' he asked, and, tight-lipped, Cathy banged the biscuit-barrel down in front of him.

Johnnie helped himself to a custard cream and munched away contentedly. Cathy could not face any more coffee and a biscuit would have choked her.

He was doing this deliberately, she knew. Trying to upset her equilibrium. Tormenting and torturing her. He knew she still cared, still found him maddeningly attractive, and he was playing on her nerves.

'No date tonight?' She spoke into the uneasy silence, and he seemed surprised, but merely shook his head as he reached for another biscuit.

'You remembered I like two sugars,' he commented, and Cathy closed her eyes in pain.

'Naturally. I could hardly forget your likes and dislikes. You always made a great show of telling me what suited you,' she said tartly, and he shot her a quick glance.

'What suited me, what turned me on, etc . . .' he murmured, and Cathy flushed.

'*Please*, Johnnie, go home!' she begged, hating herself for begging but unable to stand the mental strain a moment longer.

Her nerves were stretched almost to breaking point and when he made a sudden movement, she sprang back.

Johnnie chuckled as, arms folded across his chest, he studied her. Rather like a scientist studying some rare form of wildlife, she thought dazedly.

When he began to loosen his tie then remove his jacket, Cathy was incapable of movement, incapable of speech. She could only stare in dumb horror as he removed his gold cuff-links, then casually drew his shirt out of the waist-band of his cord slacks. As she watched, he began, very slowly, to undo his shirt buttons, his cold eyes on her all the while.

Then, when he'd undone his shirt, his long muscular fingers began to unbuckle his belt, and Cathy's eyes involuntarily followed the movement.

He stopped and Cathy blinked, trying to clear her mind, knowing she must stop him from stripping. 'Come on then!' he snapped, and she raised her dazed eyes to his.

'Get your clothes off! I can't stay the whole night!' he went on, irritably.

Cathy opened her mouth but her tongue seemed incapable of working. Her vocal cords were on strike, too. Not even Johnnie would treat her like this!

CHAPTER FOUR

AT LAST Cathy found her voice. 'No!' she said hoarsely, and Johnnie began to laugh. It was a bitter sound, and Cathy put her hands over her ears in an endeavour to shut it out.

'There was a time, Catherine the Cold, when you said "yes" loud and clear!' he taunted, and Cathy wanted to strike out.

She clenched her hands, fighting for control. She would *not* behave like a fishwife, no matter what the provocation. They'd had similar fights in the past, each seeking to destroy the other with words. Never again, she vowed.

'Please go, Johnnie,' she said evenly, having won her battle.

'What? When I'm half undressed!' he taunted, but he re-threaded his leather belt and began to button up his shirt.

Cathy was so relieved she could have cried. She *would* cry once he'd gone. If he ever got her into bed again she would be a willing captive, just as her heart was. If she could keep him at arm's length she was safe from his destructive charm. Then she remembered Leonora. Presumably after he had finished with her he intended spending the remainder of the night with Lea. Well, good luck to them both!

Numbly she watched as he shrugged into his jacket,

glad yet sorry at the same time. She loved him. And she wanted him. Oh, how she wanted him! Her need for him might yet destroy her. She had to get away. Go home for a weekend, perhaps?

The prospect of facing her mother's probing questions, their inquisitive friends, did not appeal. There was no escape. Wherever she went someone knew about Johnnie Kirkland.

'I didn't know the bearded wonder had been around,' Johnnie said casually, running a comb through the glossy black hair.

Cathy itched to run her fingers through that wild mane, and had to glance away, picking up the biscuit-barrel and hugging it to her, just to keep her hands occupied. 'If you mean Greg—no, I haven't seen him today.'

'Thought you might be satisfied and that's why I got the cold shoulder,' Johnnie said nastily, anger showing plainly on his dark face.

'One might almost think you were jealous!' she taunted, stung by his remark.

'One would be wrong!' he snapped back. 'But remember you're branded goods—*my* brand! I don't want to see that creep hanging around you again!'

Cathy flung the biscuit-barrel at him. He caught it deftly, and replaced it on the table.

She nibbled her lower lip, suddenly afraid. His temper was unpredictable. Like the sea, one minute it was blue and tranquil, the next a raging grey-green monster. With Johnnie, one never knew. He was a dangerous animal.

'Finished, have you?' His cold eyes bored into hers, and she nodded, numbly.

'I'm glad *all* my girl-friends don't behave like that,' he said casually, but Cathy wouldn't be drawn this time.

'Yes, it's just as well, isn't it?' She was proud that she even managed a faint smile. Let him believe she no longer cared how many women he had in tow. She couldn't hurt his heart but she could dent his pride a little.

He seemed about to say more but the silence lengthened between them, and Cathy longed to scream, just to relive the tension.

'I don't like your hair,' he said at last, but she merely shrugged. 'You had such lovely hair,' he went on, half to himself. 'Long and flowing it was. When you wore that white satin nightie, your long blonde hair made you look like an angel!' He gave a short laugh, and the knife turned in Cathy's heart, just remembering.

'We share a lot of memories,' she said evenly, 'we had good times as well as bad ones,' Her throat was dry and she wished she'd had coffee with him. Thinking of coffee reminded her about Peggy and the theatre tickets.

'I . . . I'll give you those theatre tickets,' she said, reaching for her bag.

'Why? I thought we had a date for next Thursday?'

'You can't be serious!' she cried. 'Peggy wasn't to know. She didn't realise . . .'

'I enjoy the theatre,' he put in, that half-smile back on his face.

'I know you do. But I'll give you the tickets and you can take . . . someone else,' Cathy insisted, but he reached out and grabbed her slender wrist.

'Don't be more stupid than you need be!' he flashed. 'I'll take you to the theatre. It will make a change—I can be myself,' he added, sounding weary, and Cathy felt the first stirrings of pity for him, which could be fatal.

'Good. Then I'll see you next Thursday,' she began, trying to extricate her wrist. His probing fingers rested on her pulse like a good doctor, and she knew he was mentally counting her pulse.

Then his thumb gently caressed the palm of her hand, the way it had done so often before, and Cathy's legs turned to jelly. An answering flame shot through her body, as he moved in for the kill.

Automatically she raised her face for his kiss, only half-hearing his triumphant laugh. Their bodies moved closer together, his hands settling easily about her waist, his dark head bent to her fair one.

His kiss moved her as his kisses in the past never did. He seemed to pour his whole heart into it, and she could almost believe that he loved her after all. Yet the past could not be so easily shrugged aside and when she recalled all the others he'd held in his arms, she began to struggle, but to no avail. His mouth punished hers, his kisses bruising now, making her mouth ache as well as her body.

Johnnie's hands moved slowly, sensuously, from her tiny waist up to her breasts, where they rested, his thumb caressing, driving her wild with need of him. That dangerous desire flamed anew, and she moaned as his lips left hers for a moment.

'Please, Johnnie, no,' she murmured, her body denying the word and screaming 'yes, yes' at him.

His lips trailed kisses all over her face and throat, his urgency becoming so obvious that Cathy knew she would capitulate. He wanted her as much as she wanted him. It no longer mattered that he didn't love her. She had sufficient love for them both. And perhaps he was serious this time. Perhaps he really *did* want her back! It was unbelievable, too many years had passed, but she clung to that hope as he cradled her in his arms and carried her swiftly through to the bedroom.

Through the mists of desire she heard him chuckle. 'It's a very small bed, Cathy!' Then she felt the bed beneath her, the springs groaning in protest as he joined her.

He began to undress her, murmuring tender love words as he did so. Cathy lay there, eyes tightly closed, not deceived by his words. She was simply a woman. Any woman would do.

A warning siren shrilled in her brain, and she pushed aside his hands. She wasn't just *any* woman! She would not be used in this way!

Pulling the edges of her blouse together, she sat up, hazel eyes darkening with fury. 'I'm not a whore, Johnnie! Don't treat me like one!' she blazed, trying to push him away.

'It would serve you right if I did!' he snapped, sitting on the edge of the bed, head bent as he tried to control his passion.

'Turns you on, does it?' he snarled, blue eyes like chips of ice as he lifted his head to look at her. 'Get some poor sod worked up then smile nicely and say "Not tonight, thank you"!'

'No!' she protested, knees drawn up to her chin protectively. 'I wanted you but I . . . I *can't*! It's been too long, Johnnie.'

'Not a suitable time perhaps?' he suggested, and she

flushed. 'You aren't on the Pill now?' he queried, and she shook her head, unable to meet his gaze.

'I would have been careful, Cathy. I don't want any embarrassing little accidents any more than you do!'

Cathy's head shot up, angrily. 'Accidents! Is that all babies are to you? Only accidents! That's all you think about, all you ever thought about—your own selfish pleasure, your own needs! What Johnnie wants, Johnnie must have and hang everybody else!' she almost spat at him.

Dark colour stained his cheeks, and Cathy was immediately contrite. She'd wanted the barb to go home but didn't want to hurt him to that extent.

'Oh, Johnnie, I'm sorry,' she began, reaching out for him tentatively, but he brushed her hand aside, and got up, adjusting his cords.

'I wish your bearded friend could see you now. You look what you are!' he said bitterly.

She heard her flat door slam as he left. For a moment she could not move. She was drained of all emotion. And deep inside her need for Johnnie's body gnawed at her. In denying him she was denying herself, and bitter tears began to fall. The sobs racked her slender body until at last she slept, exhausted.

Somehow Cathy got through the rest of that dreadful week, all the while longing for the peace of the weekend. From two o'clock on Friday she was free until Monday morning yet could she ever again be free? With Johnnie practically on her doorstep she didn't feel safe. After the rebuff she'd given him he probably wouldn't try again, but with Johnnie one never knew.

She didn't want to go home. For Greg's sake she could not go out with him, even if he asked. Johnnie had said she must keep away from her bearded friend and she intended to do so. He would make life very difficult for Greg if she disobeyed him.

Keeping away from Greg was easier said than done, and his smiling face appeared at her office-door bright and early on Friday morning. 'Is it all right for Sunday? Had you anything special booked? he asked, and Cathy's numb brain couldn't take in what he meant at first.

Seeing her puzzled frown, he added: 'You promised to talk to Emma for me—about nursing, I mean.'

Light dawned and she wished it hadn't. 'Yes, yes, I did promise,' she murmured, not sure that she'd said definitely. 'What was that about Sunday?'

'Sunday lunch. Thought you might enjoy some real home cooking!' Greg laughed, grey eyes twinkling. 'Yours truly is doing the cooking and Emma's being chef's assistant! Also washer-up,' he added, 'so you won't need to lift a finger.'

Cathy toyed with her biro, not knowing how she was going to refuse.

'Cathy, look at me,' Greg ordered.

Surprised, Cathy did as she was bid. The tender expression on his face upset, unnerved her, and she dropped her gaze. 'I can't come, Greg. I'm sorry.'

'You promised and I told Emma,' he said softly. 'Please, Cathy. You can't let Emma down,' he pleaded. 'She's gone off acting now and with a bit of luck you can steer her in the direction of nursing again. If you can't do it for Emma, do it for your profession. Nurses are in short supply!' he went on, cajoling, and Cathy raised anguished eyes to his.

'I *can't*, Greg! He . . . Johnnie says I haven't to see you again, and I have to obey him. For *your* sake,' she emphasised, willing him to understand.

He leant over the desk, his dear kind face only inches from her own. 'Listen to me, Cathy. If this chap has some sort of hold on you, now is the time to break it. With *my* help,' he added.

Wearily, she shook her head. 'It's something I can't break. The ties of love are strong. I still love him.'

He sighed. 'Love! It's an over-used four-letter word, Cathy! From the way he has apparently treated you I should think love is the last word he'd used.'

Annoyed, Cathy rose. 'Look, Greg, I've told you— for your own sake I can't meet you again. It isn't as if I've ever said I could . . . become fond of you,' she faltered. 'I haven't led you on.'

'No, but I've hoped you might!' he chuckled.

In the end, she hadn't the heart to refuse. If it was just a case of going out with Greg she would have said no. But there was his daughter to consider. If Cathy let her down, Emma might be put off nursing for good. She would be hurt and angry that a nurse had failed to keep her promise.

Sunday lunch would make a nice break anyway, Cathy thought, relieved that her most traumatic week yet was nearly over.

When she made her final rounds just after lunch on Friday, she met Mrs Smith, her immediate superior.

'I was just on my way to see you, Cathy. Felt like a walk!' Hazel Smith laughed.

Cathy liked her. She was a favourite with nurses and patients alike and was never too busy to answer anyone's queries, no matter how unimportant the question or questioner might see. Cathy fell into step with her.

'You've heard about Sister Nash, of course?'

Cathy nodded. 'Yes, she was supposed to be relieving Peggy Davies when she goes on holiday. I was wondering what arrangements you wanted me to make? Relief Sisters are in short supply just now.'

'Mm. I know. One of our many problems. Who says Nursing Officers don't work! I was wondering if you might fill in on Ward Three for a few days until Relief Sister Onions returns from leave?'

'Me? But what about this job?' Cathy was pleased at the thought of returning to her own ward but could not be expected to do the Number Seven's job as well.

Mrs Smith pursed her lips, thoughtfully. 'That is rather a problem, but I think Miss Snow and I might just manage between us. You would have to fill in as necessary, particularly at weekends, but the rest of the time you could become Sister again. How do you feel about it?'

From the smile on Cathy's face, the answer was obvious, and Cathy promised to return to the SNO's office after her rounds, to finalise the position.

Back to Ward Three! It was too good to be true. Back to Staff Nurse Elliott, who might expect to be acting-up in Peggy's absence. That was not so good. Yet Staff Nurse was a mature woman and Cathy felt sure they could come to some mutually agreeable arrangement. It would not be for long, in any case.

Mrs Smith took it upon herself to inform Staff Nurse Elliott of the new arrangements, which was perhaps as well. She would be more tactful, Cathy reflected, relieved at the smoothness of the change-over.

It was agreed that Staff Nurse would hold the fort on Sunday even though Cathy wouldn't have minded working. For one thing it would let her out of the Sunday lunch date and for another it was likely that the Staff Nurse had plans for Sunday, but the SNO was adamant that Cathy must have the whole weekend.

'You've been working too hard, Cathy,' she said, as they parted. 'You seem rather peaky. Go on now and enjoy your weekend!'

Cathy smiled sadly. If only she could!

She passed the nurses's notice-board on her way back to her own office and, as always, she glanced at the notices, always keen to keep in touch with whatever affected the staff. There were the usual 'for sale' cards but a large notice in red crayon caught her eyes and she moved closer.

'NURSES UNITE! MORE PAY AND BETTER TREATMENT FOR ALL!' she read. In smaller letters it gave advance warning of a protest march and it crossed Cathy's mind that the visit from those three students earlier had something to do with that.

She shrugged. It seemed harmless enough and nurses *were* underpaid and often badly treated. If they wanted to march and wave banners, good luck to them. As long as the patients did not suffer, that was the all-important proviso.

Nevertheless, she made a note to seek out Student Nurse Ann Ives on Monday and find out more. If she wasn't so senior she, too, might be marching!

Friday evening Cathy called on Peggy again and they had supper together. Although Johnnie's house was so near, Cathy resolutely refused to drive past it. She wanted nothing further to do with the man. She was convinced of that. At least her brain was. Convincing her heart was another matter!

On Saturday, Cathy just mooned around, cleaning her flatlet in a desolutory way. She who had once been so house-proud. Then she cleaned the Mini for good measure, the exercise bringing colour to her normally pale cheeks. She badly needed a holiday, her last one being in January. June was on the verge of busting out all over and she had two weeks booked at the end of the month, but no plans to go away.

Having rich parents, Cathy had been everywhere during her childhood and teens. She'd seen most of Europe, a good deal of England and Wales plus a ski-ing trip to Scotland while she was still at school. She accompanied her parents to the United States on several occasions, and once to the Caribbean. Of course there was a whole lot of world left but there were not many places she could visit for only two weeks.

She would naturally go home for a few days, try to persuade her company-director father to take things easy. Something she knew he was incapable of doing. But that meant facing a barrage of questions about her private life, mainly from her mother. Mother had idolised Johnnie and Cathy did not intend to tell her that he was here in Bellington. She would be hurt that he hadn't bothered to keep in touch after the break-up. Cathy's parents did so much for Johnnie—now he did not want to know, and Cathy's anger against him mounted. He wasn't worth crying over, but she'd made the mistake of falling for a worthless man. Now she was reaping the bitter harvest.

Sunday lunch was everything Cathy had hoped it would be. Greg's daughter gave her a warm kiss on the cheek. Cathy hoped it was simply part of her 'actress' phase, and not a welcome to a prospective stepmother!

Cathy had taken pains with her outfit, wanting to look nice for Emma, yet anxious to bring her senior nurse image with her. After all, that was the reason for the invitation. She wore a plain blue shirtwaister and carried a cream cardigan, in case the weather blew up. She wasn't going to take her car, as Greg had promised to call for her about noon.

She wore no jewellery except the locket, which she tucked inside her dress. If anyone had opened it they would have been surprised to find it empty, for Cathy never carried Johnnie's photograph about. Indeed, she kept only one of him—a close-up she'd persuaded him to have taken professionally. That she kept locked in her bureau at her parent's home. Here at the District she wanted no reminders. Yet she always wore the locket. She could not give it up and she'd tried. Once she even swam out to sea with it, intending to consign it to the deep, but she still wore it after her swim. It was part of Johnnie and she could not throw it away.

All she had of him at home was the photograph and a
pair of his cufflinks, set with a minute diamond. They
were a birthday present to him from her parents. If he
missed them when he packed he gave no sign, and she
hung onto them. He'd worn them only once as far as she
knew, but he might well have worn them when he was
out with other women.

Cathy flinched at the painful thought. Even her best
friend had seen him. Brenda Chalmers wouldn't lie.
She'd never cared for Johnnie and often warned Cathy
about his philandering ways. Cathy shut out the voice
from the past, and was relieved when Greg had arrived
early.

She'd let him in cautiously, fearing that Johnnie would
be behind him. He might be away, perhaps camping
out in his new house. Perhaps in an hotel with Leonora or this early-rising girl-friend he'd mentioned.
Well, she didn't care! She was going to enjoy what re-
mained of her weekend and to hell with Johnnie Kirkland!

They lingered over their pre-lunch drink while Emma
put a few finishing touches to the meal, yet spoke of
impersonal, hospital matters. Cathy wanted to raise no
false hopes. It wasn't fair to Greg. She should never
have gone out with him in the first place but she was
human. She wouldn't have been a woman if she hadn't
been flattered by his persistence, his dogged pursuit of
her.

Lunch was roast chicken served with boiled potatoes
and a tangy sauce which Greg proudly claimed to have
made himself.

'Should have been a chef, if I say so myself!' he

smirked, and she and Emma exchanged fond glances.

It was so like a family, a *real* family, and Cathy wanted to weep. They both made her so welcome, drawing her into their charmed circle, and she felt an impostor. She didn't belong yet she felt the bonds of family life pulling her in, tying her to father and daughter.

They served ice-cream for pudding, and Cathy didn't have room for the enormous helping Emma handed out.

'I can't! I'm sure I shall burst!' she protested, but Emma looked crestfallen so Cathy valiantly tucked into the ice-cream and was almost finished when the telephone rang.

'It's your turn, Dad,' Emma said firmly. 'I answered it yesterday.'

'It's probably one of your millions of young men,' her father grumbled, with a wink for Cathy.

'Dad's a pet but he needs organising,' Emma said lightly, while Greg answered the telephone in the hall.

Cathy winced, and turned the conversation to nursing. Emma was giving her views on the subject when a grey-faced Greg returned.

'Greg? What is it?' Cathy rose, but he gently pushed her down again.

'It's for you, Cathy. Dr Kirkland desires a word with you,' he said heavily.

Cathy went white. Johnnie knew! 'But he doesn't know I'm here! How could he? You didn't tell him?'

'He asked to speak to Sister Grainger. I told him you weren't here but he wouldn't believe me. When he said he had a message from home for you, an urgent message, I had to admit you were here. Sorry, Cathy,' he said apologetically, but Cathy was already on her way to the telephone, her nerves jangling.

CHAPTER FIVE

CATHY sat silently beside Johnnie on the drive down to Sussex. She felt numb, not of this world. Her father had suffered a heart attack, a massive one by all accounts, and was not expected to live. He might even be dead by now, she acknowledged. If victims survived the first few hours there was hope of recovery, but would he survive that long?

She felt sick now. There she was, enjoying herself, feeling as if she hadn't a care in the world except for Johnnie Kirkland, while her father was fighting for his life. Being on the receiving end, a relative instead of a nurse, was rather different, Cathy found. Her expert knowledge did not help her. She was as afraid as any of the public. She loved her father even though they'd drifted apart in recent years.

Poor Mother, too. Of course, she would survive. Marguerite Grainger was tough, resilient, rather like Cathy herself. Deceptively slender, a tiny figure, yet with hidden reserves and nerves of steel.

Cathy gazed blindly down at her hands which were tightly clenched. She felt the nails cutting into the palms, and slowly flexed her fingers. There was no point in getting up-tight. Whatever will be, will be, she chanted silently. That was what she'd told herself over and over again when Johnnie left her. If it was meant to be, there was nothing she could do. It was Fate.

A sigh escaped her, and she clenched her fists again. She wasn't a person who really believed in Fate. If her thoughts and prayers could pull her father through then he had a very good chance indeed.

'Tired, Cathy?' Johnnie shot her a quick glance before once more concentrating on driving. It was the first remark he'd addressed to her, except for the briefing he'd given on her father's condition.

He had picked her up outside Greg's house, and hadn't even bothered to get out of his car. He completely ignored Greg and Emma, but could not have failed to see Greg kiss Cathy's brow and squeeze her hand as she reluctantly got in beside Johnnie. The Mercedes shot off and Cathy was propelled forward until her numb fingers found the seat-belt. Evidently Johnnie could not wait to get away from Greg's house.

Now, she shook her head. 'I'm not really tired. More numb than anything. It's been a long while since I . . . since I saw Father,' she finished jerkily. Far too long. Pressure of work, not wanting to answer mother's searching questions, Brenda's over-sympathetic manner whenever Johnnie was mentioned—these were the excuses she'd made to herself for not going home. Without her father there would not be a home. Her mother was half-French and would most likely return to Paris, where she had many relatives.

She became aware of the car slowing down and she turned to Johnnie in protest, believing he was stopping for a snack. Then he pulled up outside a telephone box, and she understood.

She began to open the car-door but Johnnie stopped her. The touch of his hand on her shoulder sent a tremor through her and she shrugged his hand away. He mustn't touch her, he mustn't!

'For God's sake, Cathy! I'm not going to rape you! I'll phone—you stay here,' he added curtly, and reluctantly Cathy did as she was told. It was cowardly but comforting to know that Johnnie would telephone, see how things were, relieve her of some of the agony.

They were not far from home now, she saw. Another ten or fifteen minutes of driving through pretty country lanes, picturesque villages. There would even be a glimpse of the sea as they passed. Not that she cared about the scenery at that moment, but she forced herself to concentrate on it, mentally tracing the route home. It kept her mind half-occupied. Anything was better than staring at Johnnie in the phone-box. But that was what she did once she'd memorised their route. He was speaking, she saw his lips move but could not lip-read from there.

She looked away. Johnnie's silver Mercedes was parked in a lay-by off the busy main road. To their right, fields stretched interminably away. She could just see a farmhouse by craning her neck.

Why was he so long? Hurry up, Johnnie! she cried to herself. What else could she look at? She twisted around in her seat but behind was just the main road with yet more fields. The next village was just ahead, once they'd negotiated the high-banked lane, for this was where they turned off the main road. It would inevitably slow-up their journey, the roads from here on being narrow and twisting. Johnnie would get impatient, try to speed where he could get away with it. She knew his driving only too well. He was a safe driver yet impatient, demanding his own way on the roads as in everything, she thought ruefully. That was Johnnie Kirkland all over. Johnnie's needs were paramount.

He was just coming out of the phone-box as she turned back in her seat. His darkly handsome face gave nothing away. Then it never did. He kept his emotions under a tight rein except for anger. And passion. She shut her eyes, not wanting to think any more. What will be, will be, she repeated silently.

He got in beside her, slamming the door with unnecessary force, and reluctantly she opened her eyes and waited.

Strong fingers reached out for hers, entwined with them, then she knew. Both her small hands rested in his and he squeezed them tightly.

'He died soon after we left your friend's house,' Johnnie said bluntly, still holding her hands. When she made to withdraw them he held on, and she felt his strength flowing through to her.

Cathy bowed her head, unable to absorb the shock as yet. Full realisation would come when she got to the hospital.

'He was a good man,' Johnnie's deep voice was soft now.

'Father was good to you,' Cathy murmured, thinking of all he'd done for Johnnie in the past.

'Aye. That he was.' His Northern accent came over strongly for once. It did so when he was angry or deeply moved, and she was glad he felt something for her father. Then she recalled the way Johnnie had treated him, treated the whole family in recent years, and her heart hardened towards him.

Irritably, she pulled her hands free, folded her arms and stared straight ahead. It wasn't only Johnnie who was at fault, she acknowledged. She hadn't been home since Easter though she telephoned every week as a rule. She was more to blame than Johnnie. George Grainger was her father, not his.

Apportioning blame wouldn't get her anywhere and it certainly would not bring her father back. Her mother needed her now. They must hurry. She licked her dry lips, summoning up the courage to ask Johnnie to hurry home. Perhaps he would not want to come any further. He might prefer that she rang for a taxi.

She opened her mouth to speak but he anticipated her. 'Shall we carry on?'

She nodded. 'Yes please, Johnnie. Thank . . . thank you for bringing me,' she added, but he shrugged away her thanks and she crept back into her shell. He was making it painfully obvious that he couldn't wait to get rid of her. The emergency must have upset his weekend plans. It was good of him, in the circumstances.

They were soon at the busy hospital, not five minutes' drive from her parents' home, and hesitantly she asked if he wanted to go in with her. Pale blue eyes, feverishly bright, were turned on her, and she read anger there, contempt, too, perhaps. Certainly not tenderness or compassion. He couldn't wait to get back.

'No, I'll not stop. Give my regards to your mother,' he said shortly, reaching across her to open the door.

She held herself tautly, afraid his arm might brush her breasts as he leaned over, but he was careful to see that it did not. Then he drove off with not even a wave or a smile, and Cathy was left, a slightly-built, lonely figure, to make her way into the big, impersonal hospital.

Somehow the next few days passed. Cathy was given compassionate leave, then asked to take a week of her annual leave as well. Despite the staffing situation at the District, Mrs Walton readily agreed.

She needed the extra time because her mother wasn't as resilient as in earlier years. She took her husband's death badly, sitting for hours in his study, staring with unseeing eyes at the beautiful garden which was George Grainger's pride and joy when he could spare the time from business and making money. Which wasn't often, Cathy conceded, joining her mother in her lonely vigil. Tomorrow was the funeral and perhaps then Marguerite would come to terms with her loss.

'Perhaps Johnnie will be there,' Marguerite Grainger broke the silence at least, and Cathy bit her lip, not wanting to heap more misery upon her mother. Of course Johnnie wouldn't come. In any case he didn't know the date or time of the funeral. Yet he might want to pay his last respects. He'd been all but a son to George, almost as much as his own son, Peter.

Peter never liked Johnnie. They were of similar temperament, both quick to temper and equally quick to forgive. But Peter never forgave his foster-brother for the way he broke Cathy's heart. As far as she knew, Peter and Johnnie hadn't spoken or even met since. Johnnie's return would cause too much trauma, re-open too many bitter wounds. It was better as it was.

'How is he?'

Startled, Cathy brought her mind back to the present. 'Who?'

'My Johnnie, of course,' Marguerite said quietly, fixing her big green eyes unwinkingly on her daughter. 'He spoke to me. It was I who telephoned you when . . .' She broke off abruptly, and Cathy comforted her. 'When it happened,' her mother went on, her voice breaking. 'I spoke on the telephone to him. He said he did not know where you were but he had a good idea.'

Cathy flushed. Trust Johnnie to assume she was with a man! He was probably with a woman when the phone call came.

'Johnnie's fine,' Cathy assured her. 'Doing well. He's only just come to my hospital. It's his first consultant's post.'

'He will do well, that one. Johnnie was always a hard-working boy. Such determination, such . . .' Marguerite sought for the right word, her hands moving restlessly. 'Such guts! Not a pretty word, but he has guts,' she went on, her voice stronger now. 'He will come tomorrow. Then we shall be a family again.'

'We can never be a family again, Mother,' Cathy said quietly. 'Too much has happened. There are too many gaping wounds.'

'Wounds heal, Catherine. Given time they heal,' her mother said obstinately, and tears sprang unbidden to Cathy's eyes. If only it was as simple as that.

Swallowing her pride, she telephoned Johnnie later, but he wasn't in his room. There was a telephone in the Annexe and the nurse who answered hammered on his door or so she assured Cathy. Nor was he at the hospital.

The hall-porter told her he was at his new home, which was all but ready, though there was no telephone there at present. In any case he would be on duty the next day.

Cathy left a message for him. At least she had tried. If he was on duty then naturally he couldn't get down to Sussex, but he wouldn't be able to make the excuse that he didn't know when the burial was to take place.

Of course he wasn't there. The chapel was crowded out with George's friends and colleagues, the family sitting by themselves in the front pew—Cathy, her mother, Peter and his wife Veronica, a couple of cousins, but no Johnnie Kirkland.

Marguerite gave no sign that she noticed Johnnie's absence, being in a little world of her own, and Cathy was glad for her. It might be days before her mother thought back and realised her Johnnie hadn't come.

But he was there, by the graveside, when the sad procession stopped. He was hatless, head bowed, the light breeze whipping a lock of fine black hair across his brow. His eyes met Cathy's briefly, then he moved back for the family to be in the front.

Cathy's heart almost tore in two with the pain. Johnnie *was* family, he must be with the family group. Leaving her mother, who was leaning on Peter, Cathy moved towards him, then saw he was standing next to Brenda Chalmers, her lifelong friend. Brenda, a quiet studious girl, had never liked Johnnie, never trusted him, and had uttered so many dire warnings about him in the past that Cathy had lashed out verbally at her on many an occasion.

Seeing them standing companionably together, Cathy

was glad. Johnnie bent his head slighlty, listening to some comment Brenda made, and, reassured, Cathy resumed her original position. Even if Peter ignored him at least Brenda was making him feel welcome.

Johnnie came back with them to the house, an L-shaped mansion of mellowed Sussex stone and brick. Marguerite greeted him quietly and without surprise, lifting her face for his kiss. Cathy turned away, pleased for her mother yet wishing she was the one he was kissing. She longed to feel his arms about her just once more. Remembering the passionate interlude in her flatlet she felt it was just as well Johnnie wasn't kissing her. Once he touched her, she was putty in his hands. She had to be strong, resist the temptation. Johnnie *was* temptation itself and there was no future for them. He . . .

'Cathy dear. Don't upset yourself.' Brenda's soft voice broke into Cathy's traumatic musings, and she allowed herself to be comforted. 'He's at peace now,' Brenda went on.

'Oh, yes. My father. I . . .' Cathy broke off, not wanting to tell her friend that she'd been thinking about Johnnie.

'Tomorrow I thought we might tramp over the Downs. Take Biddy with us,' Brenda was saying, and Cathy tried to collect herself.

She needed to be alone. Brenda's gentle sympathy was a comfort but just now it was too much. 'I don't think so, Brenda. I need to be with Mother. Anyway, haven't you to get back to work?'

Brenda's brown eyes were sad. 'No, I left there. He—my boss, that is—we didn't get on. I'm still looking for another position but there's plenty of time. I can help you and Marguerite over this dreadful time.'

There was no hurry for Brenda to go job-hunting, Cathy knew. Her parents were wealthy and she was an only child, working because she needed to feel useful, just as Cathy did.

'Your jobs don't last long!' Cathy said, with an attempt at levity.

'No, it's the men,' Brenda conceded. 'I . . . I don't seem to get on very well with male bosses.'

'I can't think why. You're pretty enough. And you have a sense of humour.' No, that wasn't true. Brenda took herself far too seriously. She needed to open up more. Introverted people never enjoyed life, she felt. They were spectators at life's great arena, not competitors. They had only half a life. While she was here, Cathy vowed, she would make an effort to bring Brenda out more, help her join in.

A funeral was hardly a social gathering but at least there were lots of people there, and Cathy made a determined effort to introduce Brenda to those she didn't know.

Brenda, a tall, bony girl, her long dark hair tied back with a black ribbon, dutifully smiled and shook hands, but Cathy sensed that her friend would be glad to escape back to anonymity.

Johnnie stuck fast to Marguerite. Cathy saw Johnnie and Peter speak briefly, then Peter and his wife went to talk to his father's partner, leaving Johnnie to comfort Marguerite.

A sad smile flitted across Cathy's face as she watched them. Her mother, a tiny elegant figure, Johnnie, big and dark and swarthy, looming over her, protectively.

He must have moved whilst she was seeing the Vicar out, because he was lounging in the doorway, watching her, when she closed the massive oak door.

'Keeping busy, then?' His voice was harsh, and Cathy paused, her eyes darkening with uncertainty. She glanced swiftly at the whisky tumbler in his hand, wondering how much he had drunk.

He, too, glanced down at his glass, then he gave that lopsided grin she knew so well. 'No, I'm not drunk. I've had enough, mind,' he conceded. 'Peter is being generous with his drink today.'

'It isn't Peter's alcohol, it's Mother's,' Cathy pointed out.

'But young Pete will inherit the house so I suppose he inherits the whisky as well.'

Wide hazel eyes returned his penetrating gaze. 'Yes, I suppose he does.' That might become a bone of contention. Her father had willed the house half to his wife, the remaining half between herself and Peter. For Johnnie there was nothing, even though he had been a foster-son.

Cathy was sad for him. During his teens he had been a better son to her father than Peter, and it wasn't fair that he'd been left out. It hurt her probably more than it hurt Johnnie. If it affected him at all, he gave no sign. Then he never did. Whatever hurts he'd suffered in the past, he had always taken on the chin, never wept or ranted against Fate.

'I wish . . .' Cathy began, then looked away, embarrassed. It was better not to broach the subject.

'If wishes were horses,' Johnnie said lightly, draining

glass. 'Shouldn't wish for too much, my love. Blessed are those who expect nothing, for that's what they'll get!' he added, without a trace of bitterness.

She swallowed, the lump in her throat making it difficult for her to speak. Poor, poor Johnnie. Always the orphan. Rather like Heathcliff in *Wuthering Heights*. He had a Cathy, too, she recalled. That Cathy was a spoilt, wilful, selfish little madam, always wanting her own way, needing pretty things around her, using people.

She wasn't spoilt and wilful, was she? It was an unsettling thought and she quickly put it to one side. Johnnie Kirkland was no Heathcliff, that was for sure!

'Shall we take a walk?' Without waiting for her surprised nod, Johnnie took her hand and led her out into the terrace, then down the wide stone steps to the garden. His grip was comforting, but his touch as always was doing strange things to her. Gently, she extricated her hand, and he did not try to stop her.

Side by side, they strolled down the winding path beside the lush green lawn. Then they were at the stream, her father's favourite spot. The water danced and sparkled in the sun, and Cathy looked away, trying to hide the sudden rush of tears. A beautiful summer's day and George Grainger wasn't there to enjoy it.

Strong hands gripped her shoulders, as she fought to control her grief.

'Cry, Cathy, cry. It's best,' he murmured, but she shook her head, angry with herself for giving way. It was better to cry, she knew that. A proper expression of grief was important, but it was more important for her mother. Cathy had her work, mother had nothing.

'I'm all right, really,' she insisted, trying to pull away from him. His hands burned her body through the dark silk suit she wore.

This time he didn't release her. Instead, he urged her towards the little round summer-house, and once inside, his arms enfolded her and she was being kissed before she fully realised what was happening. She returned his kisses feverishly, pressing her body to his. She loved this man, needed him, wanted him. She needed the warmth and security of his embrace above all else.

With a sigh, she snuggled closer, hearing the rapid beating of his heart. On this day of all days she needed to be comforted, petted, made to feel she mattered to someone. Tomorrow she would probably be her normal efficient self, the cool Sister Grainger, taking emergencies in her stride. But for today she was simply Cathy Grainger, a woman who had lost not only a parent but also her direction. She simply did not know where to go from here. Her future was shadowed and only Johnnie could show her the way.

His kisses warmed her cold heart, but she wanted much more than kisses and that must never be. He had ground her heart into the dust before, stamping on it for good measure after he'd cracked it. Never again, she vowed, would she put herself in that vulnerable position for any man.

Restlessly, she pushed against his chest. She must get away. Her brain demanded release, though her body had other demands to make. His long arms tightened about her, his mouth nuzzling her neck, her ears. Gently, he nibbled the lobe of her ear, a favourite caress of his, and her heart jumped. Oh, how she loved him! Yet to him it meant nothing. She knew he was simply toying with her, amusing himself like a tom-cat with a defence-less mouse. He had never really cared and she could not believe that he cared now.

Johnnie swore and, startled, Cathy turned, still dazed from his caresses. Brenda stood apologetically in the entrance, an embarrassed smile on her face. 'I really am sorry, Cathy, but Marguerite was asking for you. She wants to lie down, I think.'

'Poor Mother! Thank you, Brenda,' Cathy called as she hurried towards the house.

Once her mother was settled in bed and most of the mourners had left, Cathy settled herself on the terrace, staring at the beautiful sunset. Of Johnnie there was no sign and she thought perhaps he'd slipped away, not wanting Mother to see him go. Brenda had gone home, promising to call for Cathy the next morning to see if she'd changed her mind about the Downland walk.

It might be an idea at that, she mused. Better than sitting around, brooding. Mother had Peter. He and his wife were staying another couple of days, then Veronica would stay on a while longer while Peter went back. His work could not be left indefinitely.

Veronica was a short, mousey little thing, domesti-cated, friendly. She and Marguerite got on well, even better now that Veronica was pregnant. Cathy wouldn't need to spend all her time fussing around her mother. She could always pop down every week, once she'd returned to the District. She was determined on that. No more excuses for not visiting, no more putting off until tomorrow what she ought to do today! A summer's New

Year resolution, she decided, with a quiet smile.

It was chilly now and she stood up, undecided whether to go for a stroll around the garden or go back indoors. She opted for the stroll. The fresh air might clear her head, which had been aching since the episode in the summer-house.

That man! Never would she be free of him. What Johnnie had, Johnnie kept. She ought to ring Greg. She did so the day she arrived, just to let him know how things were but a long conversation with him was just what she needed. He was fatherly and right now that was what she needed, too.

She strolled aimlessly towards the little stream. Muted birdsong followed her. It was so still, so peaceful, that she wanted to cry with the poignancy of it all. The summer-house stood, remote and lonely, and she sat there for a few minutes, believing she could hear Johnnie's voice, hear his laugh. She couldn't go on. She must leave the District, cowardly though it seemed. Being so near to Johnnie and knowing he had other interests, other women, was unbearably painful. Dr Johnnie Kirkland had won that round.

Then Johnnie's laugh rang out, more of a throaty chuckle, and, puzzled, Cathy raised her head. Surely he'd gone back?

Uncertainly, she got up. Her imagination must be stronger than she knew if it could conjure up such a convincing sound-picture of Johnnie!

Then she saw him, laughing down at Brenda Chalmers. They stood in the shade of the big willow some yards further down the garden. The back of the summer-house and the rose-hedge had screened them from her view before, and she was effectively screened from them.

Even as she watched, Johnnie roughly swept Brenda into his arms. Brenda raised her face to his, her long thin arms twining themselves around his neck, pulling his head down. The figures drew closer together, oblivious to the rest of the world.

Sick with jealousy, Cathy closed her eyes, willing the figures away, sure they must be figments of her imagination. But they were still there when she opened her eyes.

Silently, as if in a dream, the pair broke apart, then Brenda slipped her hand into Johnnie's and led him away towards the orchard, where Cathy knew it was secluded, private . . .

Somehow she stumbled back to the house, the shock too much to absorb in one go. Brenda and Johnnie! No, it wasn't possible. It couldn't be!

CHAPTER SIX

CATHY hardly slept that night. She longed for one of her mother's sleeping pills yet knew she must not succumb. Sleeping pills were habit-forming. No pill could take away the agony of seeing the man she loved in the arms of her best friend. Why, Johnnie and Brenda had never got on! Their dislike was so complete, so intense that it often puzzled her. She ought to have realised that love and hate were akin. Brenda must have fancied Johnnie all this time. So much for best friends!

Tossing and turning in the double bed, Cathy could have killed her friend at that moment. Such duplicity! And it was Brenda who had told her about Johnnie's affairs in the first place. She wanted to wring Johnnie's neck, but not until she'd wrung Brenda's!

The next morning a bleary-eyed, out-of-sorts Cathy sat on the terrace with her morning coffee. Her mother had coffee and toast in her room, but Peter and Veronica were enjoying a full breakfast in the breakfast room, waited on by the smiling housekeeper, Mrs Finch, who prepared the meals and supervised the household generally.

Cathy was still sitting there, lost in thought, when Brenda arrived. A tearful, distraught Brenda, and Cathy's heart hardened towards her. This really was the limit! Now Brenda would bear some tearful tale of Johnnie seducing her or kissing her against her will. It was the classic story of the girl who stole her best friend's man, but no way was Cathy going to be taken in. From what she'd seen last evening, Brenda was more than a willing participant, she was an eager one!

Cold-eyed, Cathy waited for Brenda to compose herself. No matter what lies Brenda told her she would not believe them.

'Cathy?' Brenda's voice was broken, hesitant, and Cathy stared straight ahead, unwilling to help her friend.

'Oh, Cathy, *please* listen! I must confess something terrible,' Brenda went on pleadingly, and Cathy forced herself to meet Brenda's gaze.

'Confess away,' she said woodenly, her heart crying silently.

'It's Johnnie. Your Johnnie,' Brenda said hesitantly and Cathy waited, wondering how Brenda would handle the situation. Whatever happened she could not disbelieve the evidence of her own eyes.

'He kissed me—yesterday evening. Near the willow tree,' Brenda hurried on. 'Oh, Cathy! Please believe me. I *am* sorry.'

'If Johnnie forced his attentions on you, he is the one who ought to be sorry,' Cathy said levelly, knowing it was untrue but expecting Brenda to leap into the opening she'd offered.

'No, no, it wasn't that way at all!' her friend said, wildly. She looked wild, too, this morning, her long dark hair loose, reaching almost to her waist, her pretty face devoid of makeup. 'I . . . I wanted him to!' she cried, and Cathy jumped up, her mouth opening but no words coming.

'Please believe me, Cathy. It was all my fault. No

blame must attach to Johnnie. He wasn't at all willing. He never liked me!' she went on, truculently. 'And I never liked him, either. It's odd, that. But whatever happens, you mustn't blame him!' she begged.

Cathy stared down at Brenda's big, bony hand. This confession wasn't what she'd expected at all. It was no use Brenda defending him. He was certainly willing from what she'd seen of the episode.

'Cathy? Do say you forgive me, but he's so . . . so handsome, so debonair. I just felt I had to kiss him and I did. But I've been tossing and turning all night, wrestling with a very large conscience! I had to confess.'

'Yes, of course. I understand.' The words were automatic, Cathy's mind already concentrating on what she would say to Johnnie when she returned to the hospital.

Brenda took a lot of reassuring that Cathy had forgiven her, and her friend began to get on Cathy's nerves. 'Please, Brenda. One apology is quite sufficient. I'm sure you couldn't help yourself. Johnnie has charm when he wants to exert it.'

'That's true enough,' Brenda said ruefully. 'Though he can't help being charming. And he wasn't in any way to blame. It was entirely my fault and I suppose he let me kiss him because he was sorry for me.'

'Don't blame him, please!' were Brenda's last words as she almost ran from the terrace, leaving a coldly furious Cathy.

Don't blame him! Of course she blamed him! She'd misjudged poor Brenda. Naturally a quiet, diffident girl like her would fall for a practised charmer like Johnnie Kirkland. The girl couldn't help it. Heaven knows she herself found it hard enough to resist him, even knowing him for what he was.

And that first time, she had not even tried to resist. She'd gone willingly into his arms and into his bed, believing that he loved her as much as she loved him. Time had proved her wrong. She only hoped Brenda hadn't succumbed to that extent.

Had they made love? she wondered throughout that day. They were making their way to a secluded part of the garden when she'd crept away. The thought of Brenda in his arms, being swept along on the swift high tide of passion, gnawed at her until her visit was over and she returned to her poky flat in the Annexe at Bellington. The more Brenda had insisted it was her own fault, the worse it looked for Johnnie, and Cathy was prepared to believe anything of him now.

There was a memo from Mrs Walton awaiting her at the hall porter's lodge when she went to check her mail. There were no other letters, and she turned the brown envelope over and over before finally opening it, wondering who in the hospital could be writing to her.

The memo was terse. Could Sister Grainger see Mrs Walton at four on the afternoon of her return. No reason, no hint of what she might want to discuss. Cathy nibbled her lip anxiously. It was lunchtime now so she had time to tidy herself, time to brood over the memo as well.

It was a hot, airless, day and Cathy longed for a cold shower. Better still, a dip in someone's swimming pool. They didn't have one at home but Brenda's family did. Because she could not have a swim there and then, Cathy began to long for one, railing against the fate that meant she had to hang round the hospital until the afternoon was nearly over. A calm blue sea with sunlight sparkling on the water, seagulls crying overhead, in the distance the cries of children making sand-castles . . .

Some daydream! Cathy smiled to herself as she closed her door and wandered through to the bedroom, stripping off her clothes as she went. She couldn't have a swim so the next best thing was a cool, scented bath. At least she had a bath to herself, small though it was. Other ranks had to make-do with just a bedsitter, sharing a bathroom with perhaps half-a-dozen others.

Afterwards, she wrapped a pink fluffy towel loosely around her and lay on the bed, staring up at the plain white ceiling. She almost drifted off to sleep, then roused herself. It wouldn't do to be late for her meeting with Matron.

Still draped in her bath-towel, she was making a cup of tea when there was a knock at the door. She hesitated, the teabag suspended in mid-air as she waited for the knock to be repeated.

It wasn't repeated and, frowning, she went to the door, opening it just a crack in case Johnnie Kirkland lurked outside.

Greg Abbott stood there, smiling uncertainly. Then the smile faded as he saw how she was dressed. His face went a dull brick-red and he began to apologise.

'Please don't, Greg. I was so hot that I had a cool bath,' she smiled. 'If you wait, I'll slip some clothes on and we'll have a cup of tea.'

'I don't really think I should, Cathy. You're in enough trouble as it is,' Greg said soberly, and her heart thudded. 'I meant to phone you, but I thought it would be easier to tell you myself,' he added, his eyes everywhere but on her scantily-clad body.

'Trouble? What . . . what have I done?' Could it have anything to do with Staff Nurse Elliott? she wondered, closing the door after begging Greg to wait outside while she dressed.

Thoughts of tea forgotten, she slipped into an old pair of jeans. A bra and an equally old T-shirt completed her attire, and she rushed to open the door again.

An uncomfortable-looking Greg stood stiffly beside Johnnie, and Cathy's eyes widened in dismay. A visit from Johnnie Kirkland was all she needed to complete her misery!

'May we come in?' Johnnie asked genially enough. But his eyes snapped at her, blue fire almost burning her.

Wearily, she stood aside for them to enter, then closed the door slowly, giving herself time to think. She couldn't cope with the two of them, she simply couldn't!

Just before the door closed, she spotted Staff Nurse Elliot passing by, her expression aloof as ever. She must have seen Cathy yet completely ignored her. Did she also see the men? Cathy believed not. Certainly there was no sign of her when the men were waiting outside the door.

Unable to put off the evil moment any longer, she turned back to her uninvited guests. Greg stood awkwardly by the sink, Johnnie lounged against the kitchen table, arms folded, that wolfish grin on his face, the expression she distrusted most of all. There was no doubt that he was having a field-day, enjoying every second.

Her temper rose and she stood, pressed against the flat-door, eyeing Johnnie distastefully. 'What do you want? Surely it can keep?'

He raised a dark brow. 'Of course. Finish your business with Mr Abbott. What I want can keep a bit longer.'

Cathy coloured, knowing only too well what Johnnie wanted. Well, he wasn't having any! Little Cathy Grainger wasn't being served up on a plate this time.

She turned to Greg, whose beard effectively hid his expression. Only his eyes bored into hers, shrewd eyes that missed nothing. 'I believe what I have to say can keep, too. Shall we both go and leave Cathy in peace?' he asked, his eyes on Johnnie now.

Johnnie shrugged, still smiling. 'We can play musical chairs all afternoon, but it doesn't help Cathy. Speak your piece, man, then go.'

Greg bristled. 'When I want your advice, I'll ask for it! You've done nothing but badger Cathy since you came! Why in heaven's name can't you leave her alone?'

Cathy's eyes went from one to the other, wishing both men a million miles away.

'Why can't I leave her alone?' Johnnie echoed. 'Could be she has hidden talents! I nearly choked when I heard she was called Catherine the Cold!' he went on, chuckling, and Cathy wished him *two* million miles away this time!

'Let's be civilised about this, shall we?' Greg said levelly, in better control of his temper than Johnnie, whose temperament included a hair-trigger temper. Johnnie wasn't a man to cross and Cathy sent Greg a warning glance but, like a stag defending his territory, Greg chose to ignore it.

'Cathy neither wants nor loves you,' he went on, coldly. 'The sooner you push off and leave her alone, the sooner she can begin a new life.'

'With you?' Johnnie asked quietly, the softness of his voice a danger signal, but Cathy was paralysed. No way could she intervene. The poor doe had to sit meekly waiting for the victor to claim her!

They mentally circled each other, and Cathy wanted to scream but couldn't manage that, either.

'Perhaps not with me,' Greg conceded. 'But she certainly doesn't need *you* around!' he added. 'Cathy is an adult. She must make her own decisions, but she's been a bundle of nerves since you turned up,' he went on, truculently, and Johnnie laughed harshly.

'Perhaps she's worried in case I reveal her murky past,' he suggested, and Greg took a step towards him, but Cathy managed to break the mental paralysis, and moved swiftly between them.

'For God's sake, go! Both of you!' she cried, edging nearer to Johnnie without realising it. 'I have to see Mrs Walton. I seem to be in some sort of trouble as it is. What would she say if she knew I had two men in here?'

Cathy wanted to scream at them, but instead put her hands over her ears, and closed her eyes, willing them to go.

'Cathy, my dear.' Greg's voice came from a distance, and Cathy ran into the sanctuary of her bedroom, drawing the curtain across the opening. It was little enough sanctuary but she couldn't take any more. Hopefully they would take the hint and go.

At last the murmur of voices died and she heard her flat-door open then close. Thank heavens! Then she stared at the thick curtain blocking her view of the kitchen. Suppose it was Greg who went out? Suppose, just suppose Johnnie was still here, waiting to pounce when she opened the curtain?

Cathy was no coward. She would have to face him sooner or later. Then there was the little matter of Brenda Chalmers to sort out with him. Taking a deep breath, she swung the curtain aside.

Nothing happened. Johnnie didn't leap out at her, and, curiously disappointed, she drew the curtain right back and came face to face with Greg, who still stood by the sink, his gaze sombre.

'Greg! I thought . . .' Her voice trailed away and she stared fixedly at the floor. She felt deflated. The adrenalin had flowed and she was prepared to do battle with Johnnie, *wanted* to do battle with him. Greg was no substitute!

'I know. You wanted me to go and Kirkland to stay,' Greg said quietly, his voice hurt, and Cathy shot him a concerned glance. She felt guilty, but could not deny the truth.

'I wanted him to stay because I had a bone to pick with him,' she said quickly, trying to ease Greg's hurt. 'I can't take much more. I . . . What was it you had to tell me?' She'd almost forgotten his reason for visiting.

'Matron's on the warpath. Honestly Cathy, I thought you had more sense!' Greg sounded exasperated but so was Cathy by now.

'For pity's sake, what have I done? Where does sense come into it?' She wanted to shake him, make him tell her in as few words as possible.

'The student demo you authorised, Cathy. You ought

to have been more careful.' Greg gazed at her reproachfully.

'What student demo?' she asked weakly, sitting on the
kitchen chair because her legs would no longer support
her. She couldn't remember anything about a demon-
stration. So much had happened to her since she was last
on duty.

'Several nurses organised a protest march. The usual
sort of thing, you know.' Greg waved his hands in the
air, trying to emphasise his point. 'That didn't matter.
Matron is used to nurses marching and waving banners,
but this time they went further. That tall Semadini girl,
she's a troublemaker,' he went on, and light dawned.

Nurse Semadini! The tall, olive-skinned student who
vaguely resembled Johnnie. Cathy recalled the incident.
The three students asking her permission to march. Or
was that what they actually asked? She frowned, but her
brain could not turn up the missing piece of the jigsaw.
Surely that was all they wanted? Little Nurse Ives had
been keen to say more but her friends had shut her
up. Cathy remembered a bit more now. Evidently
she'd given her permission for something other than a
march.

'What actually happened? I mean, what did they do
apart from march? Surely there were more than three?'

'Three? Why three?' Greg asked.

'That was the number of students who came to see
me—the Friday before my weekend off. The last day I
was on duty, in fact, because on the Sunday I was
lunching with you and . . .' And my father died, she
added silently. It seemed months ago now. 'I thought
they wanted my permission to organise a protest march,

though they ought to have seen Mrs Walton about it,' she went on thoughtfully, and Greg pounced on that remark.

'They should have but they didn't! When they were hauled up, Nurse Semadini trots out the damning words "Sister Grainger said we could". And Sister Grainger heads straight for the vat where they boil senior nurses in oil,' Greg went on grimly.

'But . . . but what did they *do*? Greg, for heaven's sake!' Her voice rose, but she was past caring. If she was to be dismissed she might as well commit a few more sins.

'If you are going to screech at me, I shan't bother to tell you!' he snapped back, making for the door.

She opened her mouth to call him back, but her pride wouldn't let her. If he was going to take that attitude, let him go!

She wandered through to the bedroom and sank down onto the bed. Her head ached and she was hot and flustered. She couldn't begin to imagine what the girls had done but it couldn't be anything too wicked. Nurse Ives was a sensible girl, even if the others were not.

Glancing at her watch she saw that it was nearly time to get ready for the dreaded meeting with Mrs Walton. Perhaps another cool bath? After her recent torment, the idea appealed, and she raised her arms above her head, slipping off the T-shirt. It was a tight fit and as she was struggling to extricate herself, she became aware of hands helping her.

Face flushed, she emerged from the T-shirt, to find Johnnie smiling mockingly at her.

'Johnnie!' she cried, pushing his hands away.

He grinned. 'I thought you would appreciate my help, Cathy. You never objected before,' he added, and Cathy blushed.

'Thank you,' she whispered.

'It was a pleasure, Sister Grainger,' he mocked. 'Your boyfriend forgot to close the door properly after him. You'll have to tell him about details like that.'

Idly, his finger traced a pattern on her thin cheek, then trailed tantalisingly down her cheek and the side of her throat.

She shivered. 'Don't, please. I have to get ready. Mrs Walton will be waiting.'

He dropped a kiss on her hot brow, and she closed her eyes, pretending just for a few seconds that the years had rolled away and she and Johnnie were young and in love. They lived only for each other and no-one and nothing could part them.

Foolish woman! Life was never like that. Certainly life with Johnnie was not. Apart from the demands of his medical career, there were other pressures, the unexplained absences, the flirtations, the love-affairs . . .

That brought Brenda Chalmers to mind, and Cathy's eyes snapped open.

'Brenda,' she said distinctly, and Johnnie smiled, that lazy, mocking smile she remembered so well.

'Ah yes, Brenda. I wondered when Poison Ivy would come into the conversation,' he said lightly, his pale blue eyes mocking her.

She took a step back. Arguing with him in such close proximity was going to be difficult.

But she had to make the effort. 'She says you and she

. . . That you kissed her when you came home for Father's funeral.'

'Mmm. I did. I didn't enjoy it but I suppose it was better than nothing,' he admitted, and Cathy wanted to hit him.

'Did . . . did Brenda make the first move? I mean, she . . .'

'What did Poison Ivy Chalmers say?' His voice was still calm but she sensed his temper rising, and she hesitated. Johnnie always resented her cross-examinations, as he called them, but she had to know.

'She says it was her fault and she's very sorry.'

'Is she?' He sounded genuinely surprised. 'That's a new one, isn't it? She kissed me, not the other way around,' he added, and Cathy nodded.

'I know. She told me. Kept apologising and saying I wasn't to blame you.'

'Good of her,' he said dryly. 'The more she blames herself, the guiltier *I* seem! And because *she* told you, you believe her. When I told you similar tales in the past you didn't believe me. I was a two-timing womaniser. A wolf, a Bluebeard. Nothing but a collector of concubines,' he went on relentlessly, and Cathy felt ashamed.

'Brenda wouldn't lie to me. She admitted the kiss was her fault. I saw you—down near the willow,' she went on, miserably. She hated this apparent third-degree but could not seem to stop.

'Enjoyed the entertainment, did you?' he asked bluntly, his mocking amusement vanishing as quickly as it came. 'We went for a walk in the orchard afterwards,' he added maliciously, and Cathy flinched.

'Yes, I saw you. Did you enjoy it?'

'It?' he taunted, and Cathy reddened, wishing she'd used another word.

'Your walk, I meant!' she snapped, embarrassed.

'You will have to use your imagination, Catherine the Cold! Brenda lacks your finesse, your passionate, abandoned nature, but the girl shows promise,' he went on, with relish.

This time she did hit him, her hand leaving a dull red mark on his dark face. Gingerly he felt his cheek. 'I don't think you fractured anything, Nurse,' he smiled nastily.

'Oh, Johnnie! I'm . . . No, I'm not sorry!' she snapped. He deserved it and more! Why should she always be the one to go down on bended knee and apologise? 'That was for all the hurt and humiliation you caused me five years ago!' she carried on, unable to keep the bitterness from her voice.

'Five years, was it? You carry a grudge a long time, Cathy,' he said quietly. 'I hurt your pride a bit, sure, but I doubt that your heart suffered. You haven't got one,' he went on accusingly, and Cathy gasped, bright spots of colour appearing on her normally pale cheeks.

'No heart? I thought you were the one without a heart! You never loved me. All you ever thought about was your own selfish pleasure!' she accused, her voice breaking. She would cry any minute if he didn't go. She couldn't take any more of his company.

'No, I never loved you,' he admitted, and her heart sank. She'd always hoped she had misjudged him but now he was spelling it out plainly enough.

'I'm glad you admit it,' she said brokenly, wishing he

would take back the words, tell her that once he'd loved her and might do so again, but he did not.

The silence lengthened and Cathy wanted to curl up and sleep. And never awaken. That was how she felt when her child, *their* child, miscarried. As if all life was at an end. Her weariness then made her yearn for a deep, unending sleep.

But she was stronger now than five years ago. Suffering had left its mark. Now she took life on the chin, would not surrender no matter what the odds. But the tiredness both mental and physical, persisted, and she lost all interest in dressing for her meeting with Matron. Her limbs would not obey her sluggish brain.

It happened so often before—the quarrels with Johnnie draining her of energy. Now it was happening again. He was a parasite, drawing off the life-giving sap. He was the Poison Ivy, not Brenda.

'No!' she said aloud. Johnnie wasn't a parasite. She loved him! Whatever had she been thinking of?

'I didn't ask but I suppose you would say no,' he commented, a bitter smile twisting his lips. His brilliant light eyes were sad. 'Your favourite word that,' he added, and Cathy nodded, ashamed that it was true.

Much as she enjoyed his lovemaking in the past, she'd refused to be used, refused to be available just when it suited him. After all there were plenty of other women for him to use. Let him slake his passionate ardour on them! It was as true now as it was five years ago, she knew. Let Lea Adams have him.

'I'll let you get on. Mustn't keep Matron waiting or she'll smack your hand, won't she!' he mocked. 'Dear Matron, I'm ever so sorry I let it get out of hand,' he went on, to her astonishment. 'I promise to be a good girl in future and look forward to being promoted,' he mimicked.

'Johnnie, please . . . I have ambition. You shouldn't mock that. After all, you are climbing the ladder. Why shouldn't I do the same?' she asked quietly, too weary to argue.

He shrugged. 'Why not? Be ambitious. Take up nursing and see the world!'

'That wasn't funny! Just because I've seen a good deal of the world, there's no need to mock!'

'I've seen the world, too. Your parents carted me around as well,' he admitted. 'Must take that boy, I suppose.' He did a passable imitation of Cathy's father and she stood, rooted to the spot. Then he shrugged and spread his hands in one of Marguerite's favourite gestures. 'Of course we must. It pleases my Catherine,' Johnnie continued, this time with a thick French accent. Then his pale eyes snapped at her. 'Always to please Catherine! Everything was to please you! They never cared about me. I was a new toy for cute little Catherine to play with!' he stormed, his face angrier than she'd ever seen it.

'Johnnie,' she began, then stopped. Mere words were inadequate and he didn't want or need her love, so she would not reach out her arms to him. She would be rebuffed or else he would take her, use her body, then toss her aside like a broken toy.

There was nothing between them now, no bridge, not even a few stepping-stones. There was no way she could assuage his hurt, but at least she understood him better now. How he must have suffered!

'You were wrong, Johnnie,' she began hesitantly, 'thinking that they never cared for you. They both did, particularly Mother. On the day of the funeral she asked for you. She was convinced you would come, that you wouldn't let her down,' she went on, unconsciously putting her small slender hand on his arm. 'She *does* care for you, Johnnie. Believe me,' she begged, but his face was closed, shuttered. Johnnie Kirkland was back in his own lost world of childhood hurts, and Cathy could not reach him.

At last he gave a wry smile. 'Better go. Bearded wonder will be coming back for his oats.' He turned to go, but Cathy caught at his arm.

'Greg doesn't get his oats, as you vulgarly put it!' she snapped, all sympathy evaporating. 'There's nothing between us. He's just a good friend. He and his daughter,' she added.

'Oh? I didn't know he had a daughter. Young, is she?'

'Not a child,' she said, unthinkingly. 'She's seventeen.'

'Sounds interesting. I'll have to look her over. You're getting a bit old,' he said, conversationally, and Cathy's eyes darkened with rage.

She raised her hand, determined to make him suffer no matter what it cost, but he forestalled her, gripping her slim wrist and twisting her arm behind her. He imprisoned her left arm when she brought that up, then swung her across his shoulder like a sack of potatoes.

'Johnnie! Let me go!' she yelled, uncaring who might hear. 'Do you hear me! Let me go!'

But Johnnie might have been deaf as he threw her down onto the bed, his body following her.

'No, Johnnie, please! she begged but this time there was no stopping him. No stopping the tide of passion that swept them along, culminating in a moment of pure joy as their bodies blended.

They were meant for each other, no matter what. That was Cathy's last coherent thought before she gave herself up to the ecstasy of his lovemaking. She soared to a great height, all weariness forgotten. This was a new beginning for them.

No-one could part them again.

CHAPTER SEVEN

CATHY lay warm and safe in Johnnie's arms. Lazily she rubbed her head against his chest, revelling in the feel of his body. She loved him. If only she could make him love her, everything would be all right between them.

But could she? How could she go about it? Presumably she wasn't lovable or he would have loved her in the past, when she was a young, dewy-eyed honey-blonde. When the years and the torments she'd suffered hadn't shown in fine lines around nose and mouth. She even had two or three grey hairs now!

She snuggled closer to his naked body. It didn't prevent him from wanting her, she mused, as his arm tightened about her, but she must have an unlovable personality. The idea hurt. The more she examined it, the more it hurt. What could it be? Perhaps it was something in Johnnie. Perhaps subconsciously he resented her, resented her family. He might come to love her in the distant future.

It was too much of a problem for her right now, and she lifted her face for a kiss.

Johnnie's sensuous mouth brushed hers lightly, then he pushed her away, chuckling quietly.

Annoyed, Cathy sat up and tweaked one of the thick dark hairs on his chest. Playfully, he slapped her hand away, his expression enigmatic. 'Time to go, Catherine the Cold.'

She pouted. 'Must you? Couldn't you stay for supper? Or we could go out?' she suggested, hopefully.

'No, it isn't me who has to go, it's you,' he corrected her. Then he chuckled again as he glanced at his watch. 'Approximately thirty-five minutes ago you were due to see the Headmistress!'

'Oh, no! Johnnie!' She grabbed his thick wrist, her glance at his wrist-watch confirming what he'd said. 'How could you let me forget?' she accused. 'You did it deliberately.'

With a cry of anguish she leapt out of the warm bed and hurriedly dressed, remembering to wear her blue-and-white striped suit because it looked more profess-ional. Not that she would be a professional much longer! Mrs Walton would be furious and she had no reasonable excuse to offer.

At last she was ready, and she glared over at him as he lay back against the pillows, arms behind his head, completely at ease. 'When you feel rested enough perhaps you would make the bed after you,' she said pointedly, knowing quite well he would not. Johnnie was not domesticated.

He smiled mockingly. 'Perhaps I will. Who knows? I'll slam the flat door after me,' he promised, and with that she had to be content.

Her heels click-clacked in the emptying corridor as she hurried to Mrs Walton's office. Of course, she ought to have phoned first, but she didn't want to lose the time. If she could just get to see the woman she could explain everything. Though she wasn't even sure what it was she had to explain. Greg had started to tell her, then went off in a huff, and Johnnie hadn't bothered at all. She could have asked him outright, but . . . But there had been other things on her mind once Johnnie touched her . . .

Ashamed of her passionate response to him, she didn't look where she was going and almost bumped into Mrs Walton.

Both drew back, shaken, then Matron's lips tightened, her generous mouth becoming a thin, hard line. 'Sister Grainger, your appointment was for four o'clock. What kept you?'

Before Cathy could make a reasonable excuse, *any* excuse rather than tell the truth, Mrs Walton almost pushed her into the office.

'I'm due at a meeting at six and I have to dash home first,' she explained, waving Cathy to a chair. 'I really haven't time to hang about waiting for ward sisters!' she went on severely, and a suitably chastened Cathy began to stammer out an apology.

Mrs Walton waved her down. 'Never mind. It isn't important. What is important is that you are in the soup, my girl!'

Cathy gasped. 'What have I done, Matron? No-one will tell me. Greg, Mr Abbott, started to, but . . .'

'Greg Abbott?' Mrs Walton's eyes narrowed suspiciously. 'Yes, I *did* hear that the two of you were keeping company,' she went on slowly, and Cathy flinched.

'Hardly "keeping company" as you put it,' she said tightly. 'He and I are friends. He took me home to meet his daughter. She wants to be a nurse,' Cathy went on quietly, as Mrs Walton raised her brows.

'I see. As long as you keep the friendship discreet, Sister. That's all I ask. I like my senior nurses to maintain a certain standard.'

Cathy murmured that she quite understood, but the PNO did not appear to be listening. She tapped her biro on her desk, deep in thought. Then her sad eyes met Cathy's. 'There was a disturbance the first week you were away, Sister Grainger. A group of learners went on a protest march. That much I can condone, even though it gives the District a bad name. However, that isn't all.' She paused, heavily, and shot Cathy a disapproving look.

'Please, Matron! Tell me the worst,' Cathy begged, wishing she could scream to relieve her feelings.

'They held a sit-in, Sister. In our local MP's garden! When asked to move, they began to chant and wave placards and only moved off when threatened with police action.'

Cathy went cold. This was all she needed. 'I can't quite . . .' she began, but was waved down again.

'You gave permission for the sit-in, Sister Grainger. Or so I am informed,' Mrs Walton went on sternly, and wildly, Cathy began to deny it.

'They—three students, that is—asked if they could go on a march and . . .' She stopped. Did they ask if they could? Was it a march or something more disruptive they had in mind? 'I understood they were holding a march and a rally, Matron,' she went on uneasily.

'Did they actually say so?'

Cathy shook her head, knowing she was in the wrong. 'I understood that was what they intended. Certainly none of them mentioned the MP,' she went on firmly. If they had she would have heard them. Although her mind was on other matters at the time, she felt sure they hadn't mentioned a sit-in.

They argued the matter out, Cathy attempting to defend herself. She admitted that because of a personal problem she hadn't given her full attention to the girls' request, and for that reason she *was* to blame for the escapade. In turn, Mrs Walton agreed that if the students had mentioned a sit-in, Cathy could hardly have failed to hear and would have turned down the idea. In any case it was Mrs Walton's place to authorise such activities unless it was an official union protest, and the students must have been aware of that.

The girls would, Mrs Walton said sternly, be dealt with. 'You will have to take more interest in what is being said to you in future, Sister,' she added, and a trembling Cathy rose to leave.

Tears were not far away as she thanked the PNO for seeing her. It was all Johnnie's fault, all of it! How the sit-in could be his fault she wasn't sure, but she intended blaming him, anyway.

The fact that she was late for her appointment *was* his fault, but she'd enjoyed the delay. There was no doubt in her mind about that!

Ward Three was quiet when Cathy returned to duty the following morning. She was no longer acting nursing officer but simply a ward sister, Peggy having gone on holiday back to Wales. Cathy would have to act-up every now and again, but Relief Sister Onions would be back soon so she intended to make the most of her time on the ward. It was so much more satisfying than being a nursing officer.

So satisfying that Cathy hummed a little tune as she

walked briskly along the corridor at seven-thirty. She wasn't due on till eight, but this first morning she would need to be early, give herself time to get to grips with the ward again.

The first person she saw as she entered her office was Johnnie Kirkland. She stopped, the tune dying in her throat. He sat comfortably on the easy-chair kept in the office especially for visitors, long muscular legs crossed, smart in his dark grey suit. A different, looser-fitting suit, she noticed. This one had no waist-coat. Why she should notice such unimportant details she couldn't imagine, but somehow his appearance, his clothes, always caught her attention. He was always immaculate, expensively dressed. He must be getting the money from somewhere—or someone.

Momentarily she closed her eyes, the idea of him being supported by a rich girl-friend was too much to bear. When she opened her eyes again they met the penetrating gaze of Staff Nurse Elliott. Her eyes went from Cathy's face to Johnnie's and back again, and a faint smile played about her thin lips.

It didn't take much imagination to guess what Sandra Elliott was thinking, and Cathy forced herself to speak casually to Johnnie, after wishing them both and the night nurse a cheery good-morning.

'Can I help you, Dr Kirkland? Or has Staff Nurse attended to you?'

A mocking gleam showed in his icy blue eyes for a moment. 'No, I was waiting for you, Sister. If I might have a word?' he indicated to the others that he wanted a private conversation with Cathy, and waited until the night nurse had closed the door before he spoke: 'How did you get on with Matron?' he asked, those penetrating eyes never leaving her face, and she blushed.

She answered his question tersely, and assured him that Mrs Walton understood and did not entirely blame her for the sit-in.

'I hope you apologised for being late,' he said, with a husky chuckle, and Cathy nodded, not trusting herself to speak.

He got up suddenly and towered above her. A little afraid, Cathy stepped back, hating herself for it.

Piercing blue eyes gazed down into her hazel ones, transfixing her. There was room for further retreat, but now she could not move. They were the only two people in the world. He moved nearer and Cathy, torn with longing, waited, her lips parted expectantly.

The shrilling of the telephone shattered the moment, reminding them that they were healers, that this was a hospital full of dedicated doctors and nurses, and that their personal feelings mattered not one jot. Healing bodies and minds was what it was all about.

Briskly, the unreality of the moment gone, she moved to the telephone. When she finished her conversation, Johnnie had gone, to be replaced by Staff Nurse Elliott, the night nurse, Angela Gaskell, and the rest of the morning shift.

From now on it was business as usual. She must put Johnnie out of her mind, and concentrate on her patients. Only they mattered.

A little later, when all administrative matters were sorted out and she'd heard the report, Cathy went around the ward introducing herself to the patients, all of whom had been admitted during her prolonged ab-

sence. After the round she intended to get Staff Nurse to
fill her in on the details, but she wanted to see the women
first, otherwise one tended to think of a new patient as
simply an acute abdomen or whatever, rather than as a
real person.

They had seven vacancies, she noted with surprise,
and a surly Sandra Elliott shrugged when Cathy mentioned it. 'It's just one of those things, Sister. This time
next week we might be overflowing at the seams. We
have been—while you were on holiday,' she went on
sharply, and Cathy's hackles rose.

'My father died suddenly, Staff Nurse. It was hardly a
holiday,' she pointed out, her voice and eyes icy.

Staff Nurse flushed, but seemed determined on a
show-down so Cathy let her go on. 'You had a holiday
afterwards, though,' she continued, her voice bitter.
'While you were away we had two deaths. And when we
were on weekend "take" there were so many admissions, I didn't know whether I was coming or going!' Her
voice rose, but Cathy made no comment. Obviously the
woman had to get it off her chest. It was therapeutic and
might help their future relationship.

But Nurse Elliott's next words did nothing to heal the
breach between them: 'The moment you come back, I
find you in the arms of your fancy-man!' she exploded,
her long narrow face contorted with rage.

Cathy's eyes widened. She couldn't for a moment
think when Staff Nurse could have seen her in Johnnie's
arms. 'You must have a vivid imagination, Staff Nurse.'
With an effort, she controlled her voice and her temper.
'When did you see me in anyone's arms?'

Staff Nurse snorted. 'The instant you step back onto

the ward you start romancing. I came on duty at seven just to see that the ward was presentable for your return. Soon afterwards who should stroll in but Dr Kirkland! He couldn't wait to see you again.'

'If he's my fancy-man surely I spent the night with him?' Cathy suggested, icily. 'If I had only just left his bed there wouldn't be any need for him to meet me in such a public place. Would there?' she demanded, and the other woman looked discomfited.

She shook her head. 'No, I suppose not.'

'Then it seems that I did *not* spend last night with him, doesn't it? Therefore, perhaps your imagination has been running away with you, Staff. This morning he had something urgent to discuss and it couldn't wait,' she went on. It wasn't a lie. He'd wanted to know Mrs Walton's reaction.

When Staff Nurse made no further comment, merely thumbing idly through the Kardex, Cathy said sharply: 'Next time you make accusations, Staff, get your facts right! Not that my private life is any concern of yours,' she went on, reflectively. 'Dr Kirkland's private life isn't, either.'

She wasn't surprised to see Sandra Elliott go red. She, too, was becoming a casualty of Johnnie's charm, the one woman Cathy would have believed immune. 'If you are keen on gaining Dr Kirkland's favours, perhaps you could ask to be put on the waiting list.' She couldn't help adding: 'There's quite a queue, though.'

Sandra Elliott looked up, her face livid. 'You didn't have to wait in a queue! He took *you* up straightaway!'

'That will do, Staff Nurse.' Cathy's voice brooked no further argument.

She was rather a plain girl, Cathy reflected, as she began on the Kardex. All brain and no beauty. But it did not mean the girl didn't have feelings. She might be in love with Johnnie or imagine herself to be. If Sandra Elliott knew him she would rapidly change her mind, Cathy thought, sourly, as she plied the nurse with questions about the patients.

The atmosphere lightened, the tension vanishing as they discussed the patients. Staff Nurse was really clever, an excellent academic nurse, Cathy thought. She could learn a lot from her. But Staff Nurse should learn, too, that patients were not clinical specimens. She must learn that they were real people and had a life away from the hospital, had problems at home, too. And often these problems affected their rate of recovery.

'This Mrs Douch,' Cathy stabbed the Kardex with her forefinger. 'What do you think of her?'

'I'm not sure,' Nurse Elliott admitted. 'She might have hospitalitis.'

'Yes, I suppose so,' Cathy said slowly. 'She's an enigma.' Marjorie Douch was in her early thirties, a very tall, thin woman, attractive, with masses of curly black hair. An extrovert personality, she quickly made friends among the other patients and was popular with the nursing staff, according to Staff Nurse. Originally she was admitted for investigations, having a long history of vomiting for no apparent reason. She had other, vaguer symptoms, and Cathy wondered aloud if it was anorexia nervosa.

Staff shook her head decisively. 'No, she hasn't got that. I think she's a malingerer, pure and simple.'

'Why are you so sure she isn't an anorexic?' Cathy

asked, puzzled by the certainty in the other's voice.

'I . . . I knew someone with the slimmers' disease. She hasn't got the florid symptoms and she's much older than the average anorexia nervosa,' Staff Nurse assured her, and Cathy let it pass. Time would tell. If it was a belated anorexia nervosa, Mrs Douch would be better off in the psychiatric unit, which was attached to the District. She might have a word with Mrs Smith, the SNO, see what she thought.

The other patients had the usual operations—a partial mastectomy, several varied gut operations, two with acute appendicitis. Only Marjorie Douch presented any great problems.

Except for Aileen O'Connor, who was due for an ileostomy. Rather a young girl for that. Aileen was, Cathy noted, a cousin of their anaesthetist, Dr Michael Curtin. 'Aileen O'Connor, Staff. Does Dr Curtin interfere at all?'

'No!' Staff Nurse gave a strangled sob and rushed out, leaving a bewildered Cathy to stare at the closed door.

If it was springtime, she could understand Sandra Elliott's strange behaviour. Spring did peculiar things to people.

It was spring when Johnnie proposed, she recalled. And he was drunk at the time, otherwise he might never have asked her. She'd turned him down then, telling him to come back in the cold light of morning and ask her again. She bit her lip, the pain of remembering too much to bear. Cold light of morning found him miles away, on a fishing trip with some young nurses, his proposal conveniently forgotten.

The anaesthetist, Dr Curtin, called to see Cathy just

before lunch. A tall, thin man of around fifty, he exuded a curiously boyish charm. His faint Irish accent brightened her morning, and he was able to give her a lot of useful information about her patient, Aileen.

'Don't you think an ileostomy is a bit drastic, Dr Curtin?' she asked, as they sat with their coffee. She'd invited Staff Nurse to join them but she had made the excuse that she wanted to teach their newest student, and Cathy couldn't force her to come. There was some friction between Dr Curtin and Staff Nurse, or so it seemed, and they must settle it themselves. Cathy had enough on her plate.

'Michael, please. Dr Curtin makes me sound old and no Irishman worth his salt is ever old!' he chuckled. His quiet charm, his laughter, were infectious, and Cathy basked in the warmth of his personality. Johnnie Kirkland's abrasive personality was trying at times, rubbing her nerves until they were raw, and she needed the peace of an undemanding friendship—a friendship rather like Greg's had been.

'All conservative measures have been tried,' Michael was saying, and Cathy brought her wandering attention back into line. Mrs Walton had already castigated her for not paying attention and she could not afford to make that mistake again. 'The poor wee girl was going downhill fast, and surgery is, I think, the only way.'

Cathy nodded sympathetically. 'Is she prepared for the inconvenience, the trauma of having an ileostomy bag? She seemed resigned to it when I had a chat with her earlier,' Cathy went on, and Michael smiled sadly.

'Resigned is about the word for it. It's a terrible thing for a young girl in her twenties, but at least she'll live.'

'Mm. We will keep a close watch on her, of course, when she comes back from the recovery room.'

They chatted for some time, Cathy mentioning Marjorie Douch to him. She wasn't his patient, of course, but a patient's emotional condition played a big part in her physical one, and too often in general hospitals little emphasis was placed on the patient's emotional needs.

All this was changing, had changed in the while Cathy had been nursing, but there was plenty of room for improvement. She and Michael touched on the subject briefly, and Cathy enjoyed the stimulation of his keen mind. It was years since she'd been close enough to a doctor to really go into medical topics in depth, and she was surprised when Staff Nurse announced that she was about to go to lunch.

'Is it that time already? Heavens!' Cathy laughed, her sharp eyes noting the way Sandra Elliott deliberately ignored Dr Curtin. 'Yes, do go to lunch, Staff. See that the first-year goes as well.' Staff Nurse disappeared quickly, and Dr Curtin rose to go.

Judging from the way he shot through the door, he was anxious to catch Sandra up and Cathy was pleased. It could be that there was a romance going on that she'd been unaware of until now. The pair had quarrelled she supposed, and that accounted for Nurse Elliott's outburst of temper this morning. Though she apparently fancied Johnnie, as well.

Cathy shrugged. Who said nurses and doctors had no private lives!

Patients, those well enough, were generally keenly interested in the staff's private lives, particularly if they scented a romance between a nurse and a doctor. It was

Mrs Albeury, one of the appendicectomy patients, who whispered to Cathy that Staff Nurse was in love.

'He'd older than her, though,' she confided, as Cathy did a round after lunch, before the ladies settled down for a nap. 'At first I thought he was her father. He's very tall, rather thin, with greying hair and a nice smile.'

'Oh? I'm very pleased for her. Perhaps we'll hear wedding bells then,' Cathy said lightly, preparing to move on to the next bed.

'Oh, no, Sister!' Mrs Albeury sounded shocked as she shook her grey head. 'He's married already. I heard one of the domestics say so. He's a doctor, you know.'

With a non-committal smile, Cathy moved on. That complicated matters. Poor Nurse Elliott's hopes seemed doomed to failure.

She kept Aileen O'Connor till last, even though the bed was nearest the office. The girl wasn't Irish, despite her name, telling Cathy with a grave smile that she came from the English branch of the family. 'There's an awful lot of us. I've got five sisters and three brothers!'

Cathy tried to draw the girl out, make her talk about her hopes, her plans for the future.

'What future, Sister?' Her voice was bitter. She lay back with her eyes closed. Aileen was a pretty girl with reddish hair and blue eyes. Very thin, almost skeletal, but with small hands and delicate bone structure. If she was well she could have been a stunning-looking young woman, Cathy thought, sad because there was no way the serious operation could be avoided.

'What does your cousin think?' she asked, and Aileen's eyes opened. 'Now you're here he will come every day, but when Staff Nurse was in charge he found it awkward,' she said. 'He came, of course. We were always close. He's been in England a long time. He's my second cousin, almost like a father to me,' she added. 'He agrees that there seems no alternative to the op, but . . .'

Cathy waited, her eyes conveying her sympathy. If Aileen wasn't psychologically prepared for the operation, it might be better put off.

'I don't want it done, Sister!' Aileen burst out, and Cathy patted her hand, aware how inadequate mere words would be. She let Aileen grip her by the wrists, waiting until the girl became calmer.

'I understand how you feel, Aileen, but a long delay could be fatal, you know,' she said gently, as Aileen lay back again. 'Mr Redford wouldn't have suggested it unless all other treatments had failed.'

Aileen did not reply, and Cathy sat by her bed for a long while, as the other patients settled down for their afternoon rest before visiting time. 'Do you have many visitors? Your mother, perhaps?'

She shook her head. 'She wanted to visit, but Staff Nurse said better not. She gets so worked up and I suppose it makes me worse,' Aileen admitted.

'I think Staff Nurse was right. Your mother can visit afterwards. Who comes, apart from cousin Michael?'

'My father came once, but I haven't wanted to see anyone else. My brothers and sisters are all noisy. They're an untidy lot, too,' she said with feeling. 'I'm the only one who is different. I'm obsessively tidy and that's a great failing according to Michael! I worry a lot, too. Michael says worrying makes the colitis worse. Does it?'

Glad that she was taking an interest, Cathy explained

in simple terms about the disease and how it was believed to be partly psychological. 'But it's the chicken
and the egg riddle, Aileen,' she finished. 'Which came
first—the nervous symptoms or the actual disease?'

Aileen appeared comforted at last. and Cathy made
her way to the office, her mind already on the problems
of the next day. There were two admissions booked, and
they were on 'take' so anything could happen. Then Mr
Redford's firm were operating. He was doing a round
this afternoon, so she would have to get cracking.

In the event, Cathy found herself doing more than she
intended, as Staff Nurse seemed to be on a go-slow after
the first spurt of the morning. Cathy found it necessary
to remind her on several occasions of jobs to be done.
She felt guilty about it. Staff Nurse was usually so
efficient and it seemed niggardly to check her about little
things.

But the ward came first and whatever clash of person-
alities there was, the patients must not be allowed to
suffer. The question of the forgotten injection for Miss
Elton brought matters to a head and Cathy gave Sandra
Elliott the tongue-lashing she richly deserved.

She had the nurse into the office and tried not to raise
her voice, but obviously word got around that Staff
Nurse had been given a dressing-down. It would not
have surprised Cathy if the woman herself hadn't spread
the word, hoping to enlist sympathy. However, Staff
Nurse did not get any sympathy from the others, because
she was unpopular. Her super-efficient and often unkind
attitude to her fellow nurses, particularly very junior
ones, told against her. Cathy saw her later in the afternoon, heading for the sluice, her shoulders shaking and

she suppressed the urge to call after her. A good cry in the privacy of the sluice might do Staff good. Cathy made sure that the junior nurses stayed up the other end of the ward until she judged Sandra Elliott had dried her tears.

Just before she went off-duty, she got the junior to make two cups of coffee and she invited Staff Nurse to join her.

Sandra seemed about to refuse, but Cathy wouldn't be denied and they sat in an uneasy silence while they sipped the scalding coffee. Cathy mentally went over the events of the day, hoping the nurse would be the first to break the silence. Mr Redford's ward-round went smoothly. She'd spoken to him at length about Aileen O'Connor's fears, her unspoken wish to postpone the operation. Then he had a long telephone conversation with Dr Curtin. Both men agreed it was for the best and Cathy reluctantly accepted their decision. Still she wasn't happy, but it was no use discussing that with Staff Nurse, who refused to believe patients had real fears.

The rest of the patients were fine, including Marjorie Douch. She had, though, vomited again. Miss Elton insisted that she'd seen Mrs Douch induce the vomiting herself by putting her fingers down her throat. Cathy mentioned this to Mr Redford and he'd nodded sagely, he and his registrar exchanging glances, so evidently they were not surprised.

A weary Cathy decided she must be the first to break the uncomfortable silence between herself and Sandra, and was about to comment on Mrs Douch when there was a knock and Dr Curtin poked his head around the door, a smile on his lips until he saw Sandra Elliott.

Cathy, uncomfortable, rose, as did Staff Nurse. His eyes were on Sandra and Cathy didn't quite know what to do. Ought she to leave them alone, making some excuse to leave the office, or was that too obvious? Deciding it was, Cathy smiled at the consultant and asked if he wished to speak to her or to her Staff Nurse.

Dr Curtin passed a bony hand across his eyes in a weary gesture, and Sandra tentatively reached out as if to lead him to a chair, then drew back sharply, her hands dropping to her sides. Cathy could almost feel her mental anguish. Love was exceedingly painful. It was supposed to bring joy but it seemed to her that for every ounce of joy in loving a man, there was a pound of sorrow and despair!

'Er, I just wanted a quick word about Aileen,' he muttered, and Staff Nurse drew herself up, proudly.

'In that case I'll be getting on, Sister. There are one or two things I have to check before I go.' With that, she brushed past the anaesthetist and closed the door noisily behind her.

Michael gave a long-drawn-out sigh, then smiled at Cathy. 'That's that, then. Perhaps she's anti-Irish. Certainly seems that way lately,' he went on ruefully, settling himself in Cathy's chair.

She moved to the visitor's easy-chair, feeling unable to comment. If he *was* married, then there was no point in her trying to play Cupid. 'You wanted to say something about Aileen,' she prompted, anxious to get away from the problems of the day. Her head ached, in fact her whole face ached and she was terribly tired. Tired or not, she must listen to Dr Curtin in case it was something important.

But it turned out not to be. Michael was, she decided, lonely and out-of-sorts and needed someone to talk to. Certainly he mentioned Aileen, telling Cathy something of the girl's background. Then he went on to talk about Ireland and his boyhood there.

'Tis a beautiful green land, Cathy dear.' The endearment slipped out unnoticed by either of them. 'Green and fresh and lovely. We've no snakes in Ireland, you know,' he assured her proudly, and she laughed.

'That's because it is so wet there, they all emigrated to England!' she said firmly.

'You're good for me!' he chuckled. 'I haven't laughed so much for months.'

Time passed without their being aware of it, and they were still talking nearly an hour later when the State Enrolled Nurse, Marie-Louise Andrews, hurried in to answer the telephone.

Cathy was about to pick up the receiver, when the SEN burst in, and the nurse's large dark eyes went from Cathy to Michael, then she shrugged. 'Ah, Sister! I did not know you were still here!' With a laugh, she bounced out again in her usual manner, and Cathy mentally slapped herself for spending so long closeted with Michael Curtin. It would lead to gossip which might find its way to Matron's ear. It would do nothing to heal the breach between her and Staff Nurse. And more important, if Johnnie got to hear about it, he would blow a gasket!

Johnnie's punishments were something Cathy had never forgotten. Her voice trembled as she spoke into the telephone. She was beginning to wish she had never come back.

Michael crept away whilst Cathy was on the telephone and she herself hurried away after a few quick words with the SEN. She let Marie-Louise know that she was concerned about Aileen and wanted to be kept in the picture if anything should change, even at night.

Although Cathy slept badly, nothing happened to disturb her night other than her own bad dreams, which finally drove her from bed at three a.m. She made herself some hot milk, taking the milk and a novel back to bed with her. Her thoughts were not on Aileen or Michael, not even on work at all. Her concentration was minimal that time in the morning but what coherent thoughts she had were of Johnnie Kirkland. She needed his arms about her, wanted his body beside her in her lonely bed.

Dry-eyed, but wishing she could cry, Cathy sipped her hot milk. If Johnnie had not yet moved into his house he must still be sleeping in the Annexe. She knew now that his flatlet, similar to her own, was on the floor above. She glanced up at the dingy ceiling, her heart calling to him to come down and comfort her.

She was only yards away from the man she loved but it might as well have been thousands of miles. There was no way she could reach out and touch him. Whatever his feelings in the past, he'd made it plain that little Cathy Grainger no longer mattered.

CHAPTER EIGHT

MR REDFORD's operating day. That was Cathy's first thought when the alarm clock dragged her from the uneasy doze into which she'd fallen. Six-thirty. Far too early to get up, she thought, irritably. She'd had barely three hours' sleep since her middle-of-the-night beverage, and she didn't feel she could face the day.

She was washed and dressed before seven o'clock, though, and debating whether or not she could face breakfast, when a discreet knocking at her door startled her. For one heart-stopping moment she believed it was Johnnie, but it was a female voice that called. Sister Grainger was wanted on the telephone urgently.

Hurriedly slipping into her duty shoes, Cathy ran downstairs to the telephone.

Night Sister's voice was calm, unflurried. 'It's Aileen O'Connor, Cathy. She has been lying awake most of the night, despite sedation. I don't think she could have had much of *that*,' Night Sister went on, dryly. 'Anyway, she is adamant that she won't have the op. Says she's too young to be lumbered with a bag. Can't blame the girl.'

'No, I don't. I thought the operation drastic, but Mr Redford insisted. He said she would die otherwise,' Cathy commented. 'Is Michael . . . Dr Curtin there?'

Sister Russell chuckled. 'Aha! Someone said you were throwing yourself at him! He's married, I thought?'

'I can well imagine where *that* rumour started!' Cathy

snapped. 'He's Aileen's cousin, and could probably calm her. That's why I asked!'

'All right, Cathy. Don't work yourself up into a tantrum,' Night Sister said placidly. 'I didn't believe it for a moment. I know which man Catherine the Cold fancies!' she laughed.

Cathy felt as cold as her nickname suggested. 'That isn't true, either. It isn't my fault if Dr Kirkland sometimes comes onto the ward.'

There was silence at the other end. 'Dr Kirkland? *You* fancy Johnnie Kirkland? My God! How many more do you want? I was talking about Greg Abbott. The grapevine hasn't got around to telling me about the handsome Geordie Johnnie yet. But it will!' Night Sister said cheerily, and Cathy could have bitten out her tongue. The District grapevine didn't need any help from her.

Cathy hurried out into the cold June morning. The air was fresh and keen as she took a short-cut across the courtyard. Just lately the weather had been so chilly that it was hard to believe it was flaming June, and the chill of the morning only served to depress her further. Nothing was going right these days, she reflected morosely. All her setbacks, whether in the hospital or in her private life, stemmed from the arrival of Johnnie Kirkland and she wished to heaven he would go back to the North!

Aileen was pale-faced but calm when Cathy popped her head around the ward-door. Michael was due on the ward shortly, according to Sister Russell, but in the meantime Cathy had to do her best.

Cathy let Aileen do the talking, contenting herself

with making comments at intervals. She held Aileen's slim hand which seemed almost fleshless. It was possible to see the outline of her bones, rather as in a patient with anorexia nervosa. Both disorders, Cathy felt, stemmed partly from the personality of the patient. In Aileen's case she was conscientious, a born worrier. Also she was obsessional, particularly about tidiness, something she had already admitted to Cathy.

When Michael arrived his broad smile brightened the morning for both girls, and soon all three were deep in conversation. Cathy had left a message with the night nurse that Staff Nurse Elliott should take charge of the ward for the time being. Putting Aileen into a receptive frame of mind was top priority as far as Cathy was concerned. The girl was weak and might not survive the op if she wasn't mentally prepared for it. Cathy put great store on getting the patients into the right frame of mind for their operations and had often been congratulated when patients came through their ordeal successfully— patients who were thought likely to die.

The anaesthetist did not, to Cathy's surprise, try to persuade Aileen one way or the other. He simply talked, breaking off when it appeared Aileen wanted to speak. There were long, pregnant pauses, but he made no effort to speak into the waiting silence, and Cathy took her cue from him.

One of the juniors asked if they wanted coffee and Cathy took her aside, explaining quietly that Miss O' Connor was for operation and it would not be a kindness if they drank in front of her, knowing she was nil by mouth.

When she turned back to the patient, Michael looked

up, his eyes laughing at her. 'It's all systems go, Cathy my love. Little Aileen has turned up trumps!'

Cathy smiled tremulously, relieved beyond belief, then a new, cold voice broke in: 'I hope I'm not interrupting anything, Cathy my love?' Johnnie Kirkland strode in, face like thunder, ice-blue eyes sweeping over Cathy who felt like a little girl being ticked off.

'No, no. Of course not, Doctor.' To her annoyance she found herself twittering. Her nerves were already at breaking-point and to have Johnnie hear Michael's casual endearment did nothing to help them.

'I wanted a word with you, Michael, and someone said I was bound to find you here,' Johnnie went on, gruffly.

Michael's eyes reproached him. 'I am here because this young lady is my cousin.' He indicated Aileen, who smiled shyly. 'Not because I have a yen for this darling girl,' he continued, with a warm smile for Cathy.

Johnnie visibly relaxed. 'Good. I was beginning to believe the grapevine—that Catherine the Cold is now collecting men!'

Cathy struggled to control her anger. 'My private life is no concern of yours, Dr Kirkland. Not any longer,' Cathy said firmly. 'Now perhaps the two of you wouldn't mind leaving my patient to rest. She's due for her pre-med shortly.'

She shepherded them to the door, then went back to Aileen's bed, and clasped her hand. 'You're sure now, Aileen? You're prepared for the op?'

Aileen nodded, then raised herself on one elbow, her eyes full of questions. 'Who is that tall dark and handsome doctor? I've never seen him before.'

'He's the new consultant. He's on the medical not the

surgical side, Aileen. Dr Johnnie Kirkland,' Cathy told her, and Aileen lay back again.

'He's handsome, really cute. Is he your boyfriend?'

'Not any more,' Cathy said firmly. 'Rest now, and I'll come back to see you very shortly.'

At least Johnnie's visit had awakened an interest in Aileen. It took her mind off the trauma of the operation, so Cathy supposed, grudgingly, she ought to be grateful to him.

Johnnie and Michael were talking quietly in her office, as Cathy went through the ward saying good-morning to the rest of the patients.

The rest of the morning went swiftly, with the surgeons rapidly going through their list. Aileen went down first, then would go to the recovery room until she regained consciousness. Afterwards, she would be specialled, Cathy decided, in case of complications. She made out the rota for the specialling as one nurse could not be expected to perform the task all the time. After an operation like Aileen's it was important to have continuity, though, so SEN Andrews was booked for the first period and would keep an eye on the patient from time to time even when another nurse was doing the actual specialling.

Apart from Aileen there were a number of smaller ops, and a cholecystectomy on Mrs Williams, a grossly over-weight woman of forty-five, who had stones in the gallbladder.

Aileen still hadn't returned to the ward by the time Cathy went to lunch, a lunch she promised herself would be short. On operation days it was always difficult to get a full break. Staff Nurse Elliott was late back from first lunch, which didn't help matters, and when Cathy coldly pointed this out, Staff was off-hand almost to the point of insolence.

There was little point in reporting the woman, Cathy decided, as she vigorously attacked the steak pie in the staff canteen. It would be yet another instance of Sister Grainger victimising Staff Nurse Elliott, or so Staff would make it seem. That woman was getting in her hair, she thought angrily, cutting her portion of pie and wishing it was Staff Nurse she was dissecting.

'Tut, tut, Sister my love! Such a temper!' Johnnie pulled out the chair opposite her but Cathy refused to look at him. He'd caused her enough pain just recently.

'Are you imagining that poor steak pie is me?' he asked mockingly, and Cathy shook her head.

'Staff Nurse Elliott is the pie!' she said truculently, and Johnnie chuckled.

'Poor Staff Nurse Elliott, then. What has she done? Stolen one of your boyfriends?' Apparently not expecting an answer, Johnnie liberally sprinkled salt on his fish and chips. 'This looks good. Is your pie real meat or that soya stuff?'

'I think it's real, Doctor,' Cathy said woodenly, reaching for the pepper-pot at the same time as Johnnie. Their fingers touched and Cathy drew her hand back as if burned.

'After you, Sister Grainger,' he said politely, eyes smiling at her.

'No, Dr Kirkland, after *you*,' she replied with mock sweetness, and he shrugged.

The pie wasn't particularly inviting in the first place

and Cathy didn't care for meat, anyway, but now she had no appetite for it at all. She made a determined effort, though, not wanting to let him know he was destroying her appetite.

'It was good yesterday afternoon, wasn't it?' he commented, as he vigorously speared a chip.

Cathy choked. She felt herself redden, as she hastily reached for her glass of water. 'How can you be so crude!' she said tightly, longing to throw the water over him.

'It isn't difficult,' he admitted, voice bland. 'It *was* good. I'd forgotten what a dream you were in bed. We must do it again sometime. Oh, hello!'

Cathy, still red-faced, glanced up at the change of inflection in his voice. Lea Adams stood smilingly by his side, then put her loaded tray down beside him. 'May I join you? Thanks,' she murmured, as Cathy moved fractionally to make room for the other woman's much longer legs.

'Johnnie dear, I wanted to tell you,' Lea leaned towards Johnnie, and Cathy dropped her gaze once more to the much-maligned steak pie. She would eat it if it killed her!

'It's about the bed,' Lea murmured, and Cathy found she couldn't eat the pie after all. She gathered a helping of peas onto her fork, trying not to listen to the conversation.

'I've found the most super tester bed!' Lea went on. 'There's plenty of room!' she trilled, and Cathy chewed the peas carefully, wondering why they tasted old and hard.

'I like big beds,' Johnnie agreed, and Lea laughed.

'You could have three or four girls in this one, Johnnie dear! Anyway, apart from the bed, I thought we . . .'

The conversation continued but Cathy managed to shut it out at last. Three or four girls, indeed! Lea wanted to be careful what she said. Johnnie might take her up on that suggestion. She started on her pudding, fruit cabinet pudding, her favourite, and had taken only one mouthful when Greg Abbott joined them.

Wildly she glanced around, wondering why the fates were against her. She saw that there were a great many more second-lunchers today, and that Greg had little choice where he sat.

Johnnie greeted him in a friendly way, and Greg seemed surprised, as was Cathy. She never would understand Johnnie and now it was too late even to try.

The conversation was desultory, with Johnnie making the biggest contribution. He seemed in remarkably good spirits and Cathy wondered why. In fact, she spent most of her brief lunch-break wondering, discarding one idea after another. The most obvious reason was that Lea had given him a good night. Or was there another woman somewhere? She didn't think Lea was the early-riser to whom he had once referred.

She stared down at her plate. She'd finished the cabinet pudding. It was on the dry side for a change, and she really wanted coffee. That did not involve queueing at the main food counter, as there was a small coffee-lounge attached to the canteen, with a separate check-out. Much as she wanted a cup of coffee she didn't want to mention it in case any of the others followed her there—particularly Greg whom she'd been trying to avoid.

Anyway, it was high time she returned to the ward. She rose, a slight, graceful figure, neat in her navy Sister's dress with its silver-buckled belt and smart white tippet. She smiled vaguely at them all, trying to avoid the men's eyes, and picked up her shoulder-bag.

Johnnie snapped his fingers, and Cathy flinched. 'Sorry! I clean forgot. I've got complimentary tickets for the new show at the Congress. I thought we could make up a party.' It was a statement rather than a question and it received a less than enthusiastic response from the other three.

Cathy was the first to refuse. 'If the invitation includes me, I'll have to decline, Dr Kirkland. I don't feel at all sociable these days.' She smiled regretfully, then hurried away, aware that her refusal was terse, but unable to rectify matters. Greg caught her up before she reached the door and she turned on him in annoyance, her hazel eyes darkening.

'Leave me alone, Greg. I've nothing to say to you.' She tried to get away, but he put a restraining hand on her arm, then gently but firmly guided her through the swing-doors of the canteen and out into the courtyard.

'Listen to me,' he pleaded, as she tried to hurry, her duty-shoes making no sound as they crossed the courtyard towards a side door of the hospital. 'Let's start again. Just an innocent platonic friendship. Emma is longing for another chat with you. She's really keen on nursing now.'

Emma. Yes, she couldn't let Emma down. 'Good. I'm glad. We need all the nurses we can get,' she agreed, shaking off his hand as she went through the door.

The noise of the hospital hit them, people coming and

going, voices, a porter wheeling a patient on a trolley with a nurse holding the man's hand. Different voices, quieter now, as they approached the surgical unit. Greg was still by her side, still talking, but she scarcely heard him. Perhaps she ought to have taken Johnnie up on his invitation. They were going to the theatre together when she had those spare tickets, but her father's death had put paid to that. Seeing Johnnie and Lea together would be torture, yet she could sit near him, breathe the air he breathed, watch the way his eyes crinkled when he laughed . . .

'No,' she said aloud. The torture wasn't worth it. It was better not to go.

'May I ask what you're refusing?' Greg asked coldly, and Cathy turned her anguished gaze on him.

'I was miles away. Sorry, Greg. What was it you wanted to talk about?'

He reddened. 'I *have* been talking for the last few minutes. Apparently you weren't listening.' He sounded offended, as well he might, and Cathy felt guilty. It wasn't his fault.

'Please, Greg. Leave me. I . . . I need to be quite alone. There's a lot on my mind.' That was no lie.

The ward was quiet when Cathy returned, the women settling down for their after-lunch nap. There were only two patients for afternoon surgery and both had gone down.

Aileen O'Connor was back on the ward. Everything was satisfactory and she was awake, but sleepy. She smiled at Cathy but didn't feel like speaking. Cathy squeezed her hand gently, then went to all the other post-ops.

Marjorie Douch was due to be discharged the next day and she called petulantly to Cathy when she did the rounds. 'I wonder if I ought to have gone down for surgery, Sister?' she queried, and Cathy smiled gently, trying not to show her irritation. Who on earth would want an operation which wasn't strictly necessary?

'You seem fine to me, Mrs Douch. If only you would eat more, you would feel fitter. Perhaps a vegetarian or a wholefood diet would suit you better?' she suggested.

'Wholefood diet? I do try to lose weight but every now and again I like to tuck in. What are wholefoods?' She sounded doubtful, and Cathy hastened to reassure her.

'Nothing outlandish, Mrs Douch. Good, wholesome food—the sort you don't get in hospital canteens, I'm afraid! Wholemeal bread, wheatgerm, de-caffinated coffee, that sort of thing. I eat in wholefood restaurants when I'm off-duty sometimes,' Cathy went on. 'My favourite is oat and onion roast, but they also serve nut rissoles, pizza, cauliflower and cheese slice. Then there is fresh fruit salad, bakewell tart, yoghurt mixtures.' Cathy was warming to her subject, and Marjorie Douch appeared interested. After promising to give the woman some recipe leaflets, Cathy moved on, wishing she could cure her own problems as easily.

Staff Nurse's lunch had done nothing to improve her manner. Cathy heard her snap at the students on at least three occasions that afternoon, and she could cheerfully have choked the woman.

Michael Curtin came onto the ward later, and spent a short while with his young cousin, then joined Cathy in her office for coffee, the instant variety.

Carefully, he munched a slice of toast which a junior

had buttered for him. He hadn't stopped even for a lunch-break.

Somehow the conversation got around to hobbies and interests, and he mentioned the new show at the Congress, on the other side of Bellington. 'Why don't we make an evening of it, Sister dear? Do us both good. Come on, I need a shoulder to cry on!' he urged, half-seriously.

Cathy hesitated, her eyes sad. 'I don't feel very sociable, Michael. Really. The first opportunity I have, I must go down to Sussex to see my mother.' She went on to explain about her father's sudden death.

Michael heard her out but still insisted that an evening away from their problems would do them both good. 'Instant therapy, Cathy. Doctor's orders!' he went on, a twinkle in his eyes, and she weakened. An evening with Michael would be painless. He fancied Sandra Elliott and she fancied Johnnie Kirkland, so they would be good for each other. Michael would be balm to soothe her shattered nerves.

'What . . . what about your wife? I'm sorry—I don't mean to pry, but I'm in enough hot water as it is without being seen with a married man.'

He shrugged. 'I was a married man once, Cathy dear. But not any more. We were separated for a good many years, then she was killed in a road accident. I'm a free agent.'

Relieved, Cathy beamed at him. 'That's wonderful! I mean, I'm sorry about your wife, but I'm pleased you're free.' Wonderful news, indeed. There seemed no barrier between him and Sandra now, except Staff Nurse's own prickly nature.

He looked his surprise, his ruddy face going even pinker, whether with pleasure or embarrassment, she wasn't sure.

They made their arrangements, and Cathy had a bounce in her step as she did a last tour of the ward. She would casually mention how unhappy Sandra Elliott had been lately, how lonely the nurse was, and leave the rest to Michael's imagination. If he could cure Staff Nurse's frustration she would be a whole lot easier to work with.

Everything was on the up and up, despite Johnnie's efforts to bring her to her knees. She could survive at the District a bit longer, but once Nursing Officer Edna Burn returned from sick leave Cathy intended to give in her notice. Lea Adams was welcome to Johnnie's favours. She herself would devote the rest of her life to furthering her career—as far away from Bellington as possible.

Cathy's theatre date was for the following week, but before then she received another summons to Mrs Walton, though this time she was prepared. The Senior Nursing Officer, Hazel Smith, had a quick word with her first, over a drink in the local pub.

They were both off-duty, of course, and Cathy had had a particularly busy day, not leaving the ward until gone six. She wanted to relax in her little flat, and have a long, soothing bath and an early night. She preferred to unwind alone, but knew Mrs Smith's request was not just a social invitation.

Cathy twirled her glass around, watching the dark red liquid move, catching the light from the pub's famous chandelier. Hazel Smith peered into the depths of her lager mug as if trying to decide whether it was the genuine article.

'I don't know how you can drink the stuff.' Cathy indicated the lager, and Hazel Smith snorted.

'It's an acquired taste, my dear. Rather like the champagne and caviar you upper-classes are always tossing back!'

'Personally I don't like champagne or caviar, but I know what you mean,' Cathy agreed, unable to enjoy her drink because she wondered what the SNO had on her mind.

Eventually she found out. 'I'm not sure how the rumour started,' Hazel Smith began, 'but someone told someone else that you'd been entertaining Dr Kirkland in your room at dead of night.' Mrs Smith glanced up quickly, as if expecting to see guilt on Cathy's face.

'Is that what they say? Good luck to the rumour-mongers, then!'

The SNO sat back, startled, 'Don't you care? Don't you realise what rumours can do to a promising career? I thought you were ambitious!'

'I am,' Cathy said carefully, 'but my private life is my own, surely? As long as the patients don't suffer, does it matter *how* many men I have in my flat?'

'Well, of course it does!' Mrs Smith sounded exasperated. 'And talking of numbers, this same kind informant said you entertained Greg Abbott at all hours of the day and night. Two of them, Cathy! How many men do you need, for God's sake?'

'Don't tell me the scandal-monger left out Dr Curtin?' Cathy said bitterly, knowing perfectly well who had spread the rumours. 'Of course I haven't had him in my flatlet yet, but we spend hours closeted in the office on Ward Three. Or didn't you know that?' Her eyes were dark with anguish as she faced the SNO. 'I probably have a porter or two on the side!' she finished.

'Cathy! There's no need to be facetious!'

Cathy bit her lip, afraid that she'd antagonised the SNO now. In her present position she needed all the friends she could get, so she hastened to apologise. 'I didn't mean to make bad jokes, Mrs Smith, but it's getting too much. I knew Johnnie Kirkland before, long before he came to the District. Matron knows that,' she went on cagily, and Hazel Smith looked surprised. 'As for Greg, he and I are friends. He wanted us to be more. In fact, I think he has me in line to be the second Mrs Greg Abbott, but it's no-go,' Cathy went on firmly. 'Michael Curtin fancies Staff Nurse Elliott, of all people, but they've had some sort of quarrel and I'm trying my best to patch it up. If she's happy then perhaps she'll stop trying to ruin my career.'

Mrs Smith nodded, satisfied. 'I can well imagine that the rumours emanated from her, but once rumours start snowballing it's difficult to find the original source. You will be careful though, won't you? Once you get a reputation as a *femme fatale*, it won't be easy to lose.'

A miserable Cathy let herself into the flatlet, and slammed the door behind her, wishing she could slam the rumous instead. For a while, she wandered aimlessly from room to room, which took no time at all, then, because the evening was warm without even a hint of breeze, she decided to go out again. Where she was going she wasn't sure, but she had to escape from the hospital.

Without making any conscious choice of direction, her Mini took her to Cross Square, where Johnnie's new house was. Peggy was still in Wales so she couldn't drop in on her. She would head straight for the secluded estate where Johnnie was going to live, and drive slowly past the house. He would not be there, of course. As far as she knew he was still in the Annexe.

He *was* there, for there was a light in the front room, the heavy curtains still allowing a gleam of light to filter through. His Mercedes was parked in the driveway. Was he alone? Cathy wondered. In any case she couldn't just go up and knock on his door. She had no plausible excuse to offer. She . . .

Shaking her head, she started the car again, then a figure loomed in front of the Mini and she held her breath, glad that both doors were locked. Determined not to give in without a fight if the vandal attacked, she quickly put the Mini into reverse, wanting to scream for help but realising the uselessness of it.

'Cathy?' Johnnie's voice was unmistakable, and she relaxed, letting out her pent-up breath. She was still shaking as she wound down the nearside window.

'I thought it was your car,' he commented. 'I was just leaving. Care to come inside and have a look?'

In his usual arrogant way, he didn't expect any resistance, and although Cathy toyed for a moment with the idea of refusing, she was anxious to see inside his house and doubted that she would get another opportunity.

Locking the car carefully behind her, she followed Johnnie up the concrete driveway to the house. It was only dusk, and she turned, her eyes following his gaze as he eulogised about the view from his front door.

It was beautiful. A vista of trees wound its way down to the end of the road, out of Cathy's sight. Opposite the house was a small wood, and she could hear the night-birds twittering in the trees before settling down. It was warmer than of late, and she closed her eyes, soaking up the peace of the calm, softly scented night.

For a moment she forgot Johnnie, forgot all her problems. This was truly heaven. But the beauty of the evening did not distract her for long. Johnnie's body was too close to hers, the tangy smell of his after-shave teasing her nostrils. Funny, he still used the same one, even after all these years.

Trying to appear calm and in control, she wandered into the large hall, admiring the winding staircase which was richly carpeted in a vivid emerald. The hall, too, had a carpet of the same colour, the walls being pale.

Johnnie led her into the front room, where she'd seen the light. It was a sittingroom, a long through room with french windows to the rear. 'There is a dining-room as well, but I thought I would have my meals in here. There's an alcove that would do very nicely.' He indicated the rear part of the room where a round dining-table and four chairs were already in position.

Cathy murmured her approval, letting her gaze sweep the rest of the room. It was sparsely furnished as yet, and she supposed Lea hadn't finished. Apart from a huge studio-couch in the bay window recess, there were only two armchairs, in a rich wine velvet, and a polished sideboard-cum-room divider, with shelves and alcoves for ornaments and books.

Before she could comment further, he was leading the way into the other front room and Cathy followed, her feet sinking into the rich pile of the blue and green patterned carpet. The next room was Johnnie's study. It would be used as a downstairs bedroom or a music-room, he explained, or anything else the owner wanted.

'Useful to have an extra room,' she commented, knowing it was a banal remark but hardly knowing what else to say.

He grinned, showing even white teeth, and Cathy dropped her gaze, pretending to admire the carpet in the study, there being little else to see, because apart from the curtains the room was bare.

The kitchen was a dream even to Cathy, never a domesticated girl. There was every conceivable gadget, more than in her own home, she supposed. She had never needed to take much interest in kitchens before, at least not until she and Johnnie had a flat. Then, belated-ly, she had had to learn how to cook and do the million other household jobs that she ought to have learned at her mother's knee.

He was halfway up the stairs while she still hovered in the kitchen, wishing it was *her* kitchen, wishing she might be privileged to prepare Johnnie's meals there. It was agony and she wished she'd refused his invitation, but she must go through with it, no matter what it cost.

Head held proudly, Cathy climbed the stairs, briskly, anxious to get it over with as soon as possible.

'Cathy?' Johnnie gave her a strange look, and she hoped she hadn't been thinking aloud. 'There are four bedrooms but only one bathroom,' he was saying, stand-ing aside for her to enter the room at the top of the landing. It proved to be a single bedroom, unfurnished as yet, and Cathy relaxed, able to admire the pretty rose-pink carpet with curtains to match.

Similarly in the other two rooms, one single and one double. Then she braced herself for the ordeal. Now he would show her the main bedroom, *his* bedroom, with the magnificent bed.

'That's that, I think!' he said briskly, and Cathy opened her mouth to remind him that there were two doors he hadn't opened. 'Oh, the bathroom. The lap of luxury. You'll like this, Cathy,' he boasted, his eyes mocking her as if he was aware of her discomfort.

She did indeed like the bathroom, the pale green coloured suite contrasting nicely with the silver-grey walls. A unisex bathroom rather than a strictly feminine one, like her own back in Sussex. Hers was deep pink with white carpet and curtains.

'There's a separate lavatory, of course,' he was saying, running down the stairs, and a puzzled Cathy followed him. 'Oh, I forgot to show you the downstairs cloakroom. That's always useful. Rather like the one you have at home,' he added, his expression bland.

'The whole house is lovely, Johnnie. You must have spent a lot of time and money choosing furniture.' Not that much furniture was in evidence, but the carpets and curtains alone must have cost him a small fortune. She couldn't imagine where he'd got the money. Consultants were not *that* well off.

'Have a coffee before you go?' he offered. 'Everything is turned on, all main services as they say.' He disappeared into the kitchen, and Cathy hesitated.

Why hadn't he shown her the main bedroom? Was

. . . was it possible that Lea was up there, snuggled down in that bed? No, the whole idea was ridiculous. If he had a woman in, he would try to get rid of her as soon as possible, not let her linger for coffee. If she had stopped to consider, the whole idea would have shown itself to be highly improbable, but in her tense state, she could not see that.

With a sob that was half-sorrow, half-anger, she ran from the house, leaving the front door open. With fingers that trembled, she unlocked the Mini and clambered in. The ignition fired the second time but she had to turn the car first. She risked a glance at his house as she did so, fearful that he would try to stop her.

Johnnie stood at his door, just watching. She glanced in the mirror as she headed for home. He saluted as the Mini swept out of sight. A mock salute, a fitting end to a mockery of a guided tour!

CHAPTER NINE

THE interview with Mrs Walton was short, sharp and unpleasant, as Cathy knew it would be. At least Mrs Smith had prepared her for it.

She made no attempt to defend herself against the accusation that she had men in her room at all hours of the night. She told the PNO firmly that her private life was her own business but that she would see Dr Kirkland was not seen in her flatlet again.

Mrs Walton gave her an old-fashioned look. 'Would it not be better to join him in his new home? At least prying eyes wouldn't watch your every movement.'

'I think Dr Kirkland has made other arrangements for warming his bed, Matron,' Cathy said, bitterly.

After a final warning, Cathy was allowed to leave, and she walked slowly back to Ward Three, her expression concealing her thoughts. No-one must know how she felt, being torn off a strip for having a normal love-life. It was ridiculous, the Bellington District was fairly new but unfortunately attitudes were not. Mrs Walton was old-fashioned, though always fair. Still, having *two* men in her flat at the same time was a bit much for Matron to swallow!

One of the men in her life approached as she was about to push through the ward door. Greg Abbott, his beard trimmed, looked immaculate in a dark suit and subdued tie. He generally appeared rather scruffy, preferring to wear a roll-neck sweater or his shirt open at the neck rather than a smart collar and tie, but today the difference was nothing short of remarkable, and Cathy told him so.

He beamed. 'Decided I must spruce up a bit. Women don't like scruffy, ill-kept men, do they?'

Cathy hesitated, wondering why he should care about her opinion after all this time. 'I admire a good, well-cut suit, particularly with a matching waistcoat,' she admitted. 'Most women do, I think.'

Then she realised that with his paunch he could hardly wear a waistcoat, but he appeared not to notice her gaffe. 'Emma and I . . . That is, Emma thought you might come to a little party we're giving. It's her birthday in August and she's having a teenage do then, but we thought about having a party for the old fogeys first!' he chuckled.

'I haven't been called an old fogey before, but, yes, I'd love to come to her party.' If Emma and a few others were there it would be rather nice. No chance of Greg getting her alone then. She only hoped his unusual smartness wasn't a prelude to a proposal of marriage. *That* she could do without.

The party wasn't for another two weeks, and the theatre date with Michael Curtin came before then. Aileen was making excellent progress but was still disturbed by it all, and Michael never missed a day, spending as much time on the ward with his little cousin as his work allowed.

Michael's job was a demanding one, and Cathy saw that he was always offered coffee and biscuits and a chance to relax in the office afterwards. Although not old, he was certainly no longer young, and she was concerned at his constant weary look, the shadows under his bulbous eyes getting darker and darker. Whenever possible, Cathy made sure Sandra Elliott was invited to his coffee-breaks. She was keen to bring them together and wished she could ask Michael what the trouble was between them but did not quite dare. He was a very private person underneath, just like herself, and she didn't care to pry into his personal life. If he wanted to tell her his problems he would do so in his own good time.

As she dressed for her theatre-date Cathy's mind was on the foursome Johnnie had intended making up—he and Lea, herself and Greg. She wondered which night they were going as the show was on for only a week before it continued its provincial tour. It would be just her luck if she saw Johnnie and Lea there tonight. Well, she didn't care! Her hazel eyes glinted as she carefully applied a light make-up. Let them sit nearby. Let them hold hands, too, if they wished. She no longer cared!

If she told herself any more lies, her nose would grow as long as Pinocchio's, she thought dryly. Of course she cared. She was as jealous as hell, if truth be told. Yet somehow she must hide it, from Michael as well as from Johnnie. He . . .

A quiet knock at the door heralded Michael's arrival, and she asked if he minded waiting downstairs for ther, telling him she would explain why later. With a faintly baffled smile he did as he was bid, and she closed the door again.

She just needed a spray or two of perfume then she could be on her way. Her dress was an old one she'd brought back from home. A rich red taffeta, it had a fairly low, plain neck, and romantic transparent sleeves ending in a frill of lace. She threw her genuine Acrilan 'fur' stole about her shoulders then took a final look around, making sure she'd closed all the window and left the flatlet tidy. She liked to be tidy—unlike Johnnie, who spread his clothes everywhere, his passing marked by a trail of underwear, socks, you-name-it!

Oh, hell! Why did every turning lead to Johnnie? The quiet knock came again, and, irritated, she called out that she was coming. Surely Michael could wait a bit longer?

Quickly she fastened Johnnie's locket, that empty locket, around her neck. She could not even bear to part with that. It showed what a hold the man had on her. She flung open the door, a carefree smile pinned to her lips, and Johnnie stepped past her, slamming the door behind him.

She went white, the artificial smile dying.

His pale eyes swept over her, missing nothing. He put out a strong, lean hand and touched the locket where it nestled in the crevice between her breasts. His touch burned. Shivers of excitement went right along her body, leaving her strangely on edge.

'Still wear it, I see,' he commented. Before she could stop him, he flicked it open and stared at its emptiness. 'No photographs?' he asked softly. 'You could use one side for each man.'

Her eyes sparked fire. 'They are not my men! Why can't you get that into your head?'

'No? But you keep them both dangling on a string!' he charged. 'Why the fancy dress, the plunging neckline, if it isn't a come-on? Poor old Michael will have a heart attack if you make a pass at him. He isn't in the best of health, you know.'

'No, I didn't. Is it anything serious?' she asked, thinking of Staff Nurse Elliott, but he must have misconstrued her concern, because he gripped her painfully just above the elbows, and pulled her towards him.

'Never mind Curtin! My car's at the back. We have some unfinished business!' he grated, his eyes blazing down into hers.

Frightened, she tried to escape, but his fingers tightened cruelly on her arms, and she involuntarily whimpered in pain. 'Johnnie! Please! Michael's waiting downstairs. I must go. Please?' She hated to beg but she was too frightened to go with him, wherever it was. If she could stall him long enough, Michael might come up to see what was delaying her. Johnnie would have to let her go then.

But would he? she wondered. Knowing this unpredictable man, there was likely to be a fight, or at least an unpleasant exhibition of temper. Another bad report and she would be asked to leave her flatlet, perhaps even the hospital.

Because of this, she stopped struggling, and he laughed, exultantly. 'Decided to come quietly, then?' His white teeth gleamed in the swarthiness of his face, and there was a wild light in his eyes. Cathy was immediately reminded of his youthful gipsy image. In her imagination as a child she'd believed him to be a gipsy, a genuine Romany. There was something untamed, wild, about him. She had tried leashing him and failed utterly. Johnnie belonged to no-one but himself.

Still afraid, but believing it to be the lesser of the two evils, she allowed herself to be escorted from the flatlet and down the back stairs which led to the courtyard. Michael would be waiting at the front of the building, near the car-park.

She tried once more to reason with him. 'Please Johnnie—let me just tell Michael I can't go out with him. He'll be terribly worried. And . . . Oh!' To her horror she suddenly remembered Greg. He was going to pop in with a magazine he wanted her to look through. There were a few items he wanted for Emma's birthday party, and he wanted her advice. He was supposed to meet her on the ward but must have been called away. Suppose he came tonight?

'Yes?' Johnnie's grip tightened, as he frog-marched her away. His car was parked in a side-street, away from the hospital.

'It . . . it's nothing, really,' she assured him. All three men in one evening and her reputation would be torn to shreds—what little reputation Staff Nurse Elliott had left her!

Soon she was being driven along in the direction of Cross Square. 'If we are going to your new home, Johnnie, I've already had the grand tour. Remember?' she asked sweetly, and he chuckled.

'We didn't finish the tour. I forgot to show you my room—*our* room,' he emphasised, and Cathy's eyes blazed.

'Our room! You can't seriously imagine I would share that . . . that bed with you?' He must be out of his mind, and she said so.

'Sometimes I *do* go out of my mind, Cathy,' he said

softly, and she was still puzzling over his words when the Mercedes came to a halt in the driveway of his house. 'There.' He pointed to the name-plate hanging above the door.

Cathy leaned forward, unable to believe what she saw. 'Graingers. What an odd name for a house.'

'Yes, isn't it? I like to be different, Cathy my dear!'

'Don't call me your dear!' she flung at him as he unlocked the front-door.

'Why? Curtin called you that one day. I heard the man. Am I to get only the crumbs these days? Is that all that's left, Cathy?' His voice was shaking with temper and Cathy hardened her heart against him.

'Still playing the poor little orphan, aren't you?' she said savagely, as he half-pushed her into the sittingroom. 'What poor little Johnnie wants, Johnnie must have because he's an unwanted orphan!' She almost choked on the words, refusing to sit when he pointed to one of the armchairs.

'Don't sit down then! Go to Hell for all I care!' he snapped, lines of bad temper deepening around his nose and mouth. 'Leave your bag and that furry thing here,' he went on, his voice controlled again, and Cathy was about to refuse, but his blue eyes still held that wild expression and she didn't dare enflame him more.

She put her belongings on the studio couch, and, trembling inwardly, followed him up the winding stair-case, wondering what horrors were in store for her. She was going to refuse even to look at the room, let alone go inside, but Johnnie's hand on her arm propelled her forward, and she was forced to walk into the master bedroom.

Startled, she faced Johnnie. Except for a large chest of drawers, the room was virtually empty. 'Where is all your furniture? I mean, the bed and . . . and wardrobes and things?' she hurried on.

The expression in his eyes was unfathomable. 'What bed? I haven't bought even half the furniture yet.'

'The bed Lea was describing to you one lunchtime in the canteen,' Cathy reminded him, her voice shaking.

'Oh, that bed. Well now, perhaps I turned down the offer of a tester bed. Perhaps I prefer a newer model?' he suggested coolly.

'Yes, of course. I hadn't thought,' she said in a small voice. 'It's a lovely house, Johnnie.' With an effort she managed a smile. 'I hope you will be happy here at . . . at Graingers.' She almost spat out the name of the house.

'It's a tribute to the people who took me in when no-one else wanted me,' he put in, and Cathy's face cleared. For a moment she'd thought it an oblique hurtful reference to herself.

'I didn't know you appreciated it,' she confessed. 'I thought it was a case of grab all you can, then turn your back on those who helped you up the ladder.'

He flushed, and Cathy was immediately contrite. 'Yes, that sums me up nicely, Cathy. Johnnie grab-and-run!'

He almost ran down stairs and she followed slowly, her thoughts in turmoil. He was such a contradiction. One minute he seemed just as he had described himself—Johnnie grab-and-run. The next he was saying how appreciative he was of her family, even to the extent of naming his house after them. Would she ever understand the man?

They were sitting in the kitchen drinking tea when the doorbell rang. It couldn't be said they were sitting in a companionable silence, rather it was a state of armed truce. But truce it was, and Cathy was beginning to relax, realising that whatever the reason Johnnie had brought her here it wasn't to fling her on the bed and make violent love to her. There wasn't even a bed!

But she tensed up again when the bell went. Johnnie half-rose, his brow furrowed. 'Perhaps I ought to go now,' she said firmly, seizing the chance of escape. If she stayed longer she would get too content and might even end up on the studio couch with Johnnie. Better this way.

He shrugged. 'You can, if that's what you want. Is it, Cathy?' His gaze held hers, those brilliant eyes boring into her soul, and she stammered as she told him that it was, that she must get back to her rooms.

The light in his eyes flickered, dimmed, then was extinguished. 'I'll see you out,' he said woodenly, just as the doorbell rang again. This time the person outside kept a finger on the bell and Cathy didn't want to be in his or her shoes when Johnnie opened that door. His temper, always on a short fuse, was visibly rising.

Johnnie flung open the front door, Cathy just behind him with her jacket and bag. Greg stood on the door-step, blinking in the sudden light from the hall.

'Yes?' Johnnie barked, and Cathy was amused to see Greg take a backward step.

'I . . . Ah, there you are, Cathy! Are you all right, my dear?' Greg put out a hand as if to help her out of the house, and it was her turn to retreat.

'Of course I'm all right!' she snapped at him. 'Can't I

visit an . . . an old friend without you fussing around me like a hen!'

Greg looked nonplussed, and she hastened to apologise. That sort of bitchy remark wasn't like her. It was all Johnnie's fault! He'd made her so on edge that her nerves were tightly stretched and would snap completely at any moment.

'There! See what you made me do!' She turned on a surprised Johnnie. 'I've upset Greg now. Why can't you leave me alone?'

Greg glanced from one to the other, his eyes narrowed. 'Maybe if I came in, we could conduct this conversation in a civilised manner,' he said pompously, gingerly stepping past an angry Johnnie and closing the door quietly after him. Johnnie shrugged, then led the way into the sittingroom.

'I say! This *is* nice,' Greg said appreciatively. 'That carpet is an unusual green. I like strong colours.'

'Presumably you didn't come here to admire my carpet,' Johnnie said stonily. 'So what *did* you come for?'

Greg looked surprised. 'Why, to see Cathy, naturally.'

'Naturally,' Johnnie agreed, silkily. Cathy held her breath. She could almost see Johnnie sharpening his claws before leaping upon Greg.

'I brought that teenage magazine, Cathy,' Greg said, turning to her. 'It's full of party ideas, and I thought we might get together on it. Give Emma a surprise.'

'How did you know Cathy was here?' Johnnie seemed to relax, accepting that Greg's reason for wanting to see her was innocent enough.

'Dr Curtin told me. I wandered into the Annexe and there he was, waiting in the downstairs lounge. He was beginning to get fed up with waiting, I think, so we both trooped up to your flat and there you weren't!' Greg joked.

'I suppose you're part Red Indian and can track down missing persons?' Johnnie said sarcastically, but Greg appeared not to hear the sarcasm.

'No, it was that tall, ugly Staff Nurse of yours, Cathy. Forget her name.'

'Staff Nurse Sandra Elliott,' Cathy said, clearly. 'She saw me leave with Johnnie?'

'Must have done. Unless she put two and two together and came up with the right answer!' Greg chortled.

'She's always putting two and two together,' Cathy snapped. 'If only I could get her and Michael back in each other's arms she might be easier to . . .'

'Curtin?' Johnnie broke in. 'She and Curtin are . . . friends?'

'Why, of course,' Greg put in. 'I thought everyone knew that. Still, you're new here, not in tune with the grapevine yet, I suppose. Can't think what he sees in her, can you, Cathy?'

'No, that's for sure,' Cathy said, with feeling. 'If he ever marries her, he's in for one hell of a time!'

'Marriage changes people, Cathy. Sometimes for the better.' Johnnie's voice was sad, withdrawn, and she glanced at him sharply, wishing she could read his mind.

'Are you coming back with me?' Greg asked hopefully, and Cathy nodded.

But Johnnie's hand on her wrist prevented her. 'No,

she isn't going back with you, Abbott. She's staying with me.'

'Is that what you want, Cathy?' Greg asked quietly, and she shook her head.

'No, please take me back. Let go!' That last remark was addressed to Johnnie, who refused to do anything of the kind.

'You're staying, Sister Grainger,' he said, with mock sweetness. 'I'll let you out,' he said to Greg, releasing Cathy's wrist for a moment.

She rubbed it, ruefully, knowing that by the morning she would have yet another bruise to add to the sum total. But she definitely wasn't staying to be man-handled! Whilst Johnnie was opening the door for Greg, she slipped past him and stood on the other side of Greg, hoping he would defend her.

'Cathy, come here,' Johnnie ordered, but she shook her head vehemently, the honey hair flying about her face.

'I'm going with Greg. You can't keep me here,' she said, defiantly.

'If Cathy wants to come with me, Dr Kirkland, you have no right to stop her,' Greg said firmly, and she could have hugged him.

'No, I haven't, have I? Have I, Cathy?' His voice sounded defeated and she almost weakened, but that was a favourite ploy of his. She had tried to leave him in the past, only for him to turn that orphan puppy look on her, knowing she would capitulate.

'You *have* no rights,' she repeated. 'I'm a free agent. Your spell is broken.' How I wish it was, she said to herself.

'Then I'll have to keep you here by force,' Johnnie

said suddenly, grasping her wrist and dragging her away
from the protection of Greg's body.

Though she struggled, he held her easily, grinning at
Greg. 'You'd better go, Abbott. Sister Grainger and I
have a lot to discuss tonight.'

His voice was honey-sweet, soft and warm, and Cathy
trembled as she was held against his body. Once she was
in his arms she would have no strength left to resist. It
would be another round he'd won. She could not let that
happen.

She renewed her struggles, and Greg took a step
towards them, then stopped. 'Let her go, Kirkland.
She's done you no harm!'

'Why should I? So she can warm your bed instead of
mine?' Johnnie asked silkily, and Greg reddened.

'Yes. That would be rather nice. Cathy is excellent in
bed, but I suppose you know that already,' Greg said
quietly, and Cathy's mouth dropped open in astonishment.

Johnnie released her but she made no move to escape
through the half-open door.

Grey-faced, he said: 'You told me that this . . . this
bearded wonder was only a friend!' Johnnie's eyes
glowed with a strange light, and Cathy was afraid again.
If only that light was jealousy!

'He is, Johnnie. Truly.' To Greg she said: 'Tell him
the truth, Greg. That we've never . . . never had . . . I
mean, we've never been more than friends.'

When Greg didn't answer she almost sobbed. 'For
pity's sake, *tell* him.'

She did cry then, the sobs racking her slight body.
Never had she been so unhappy, so humiliated. John-

nie's arms went around her and she clung to him, strangely at peace in his arms.

'I was right all along, Cathy.' Greg's voice seemed to come from a distance. 'He's blackmailing you. Got some kind of a hold on you.'

Johnnie's arms tightened about her, when she would have made a move towards Greg.

'Let him finish, Cathy. I'm beginning to enjoy myself. Perhaps we should close the door. We're giving the neighbours a free show.'

'Listen! Both of you,' she begged. 'Johnnie is not blackmailing me, Greg. You must believe that.'

'Then why can't you break free of him?' Greg seemed unconvinced, and Cathy could not blame him.

Ignoring Greg's question, she went on: 'And Greg and I are not lovers, Johnnie. I . . . I wouldn't. I couldn't,' she finished decisively, wishing this living nightmare was over.

'I'm glad to hear that,' Johnnie said, benignly. 'Come on, Abbott. Go home and leave us in peace. Cathy is staying the night. With me,' he said pointedly, and Cathy blushed.

His implication was all too clear. If Johnnie thought she was going to be a bed-warmer, he would have to think again!

'Surely Cathy should be allowed some say in the matter?' Greg was red-faced and clearly having a hard struggle to hold onto his temper. 'If he isn't blackmailing you, what *is* his hold over you?' He almost shouted the question.

'Go on. Tell him,' Johnnie ordered, and Cathy licked her dry lips.

'Marriage,' was all she said, and Greg looked deflated.

'Marriage? You mean you were married to this . . . this womaniser?'

She nodded, the memory of it still painful. 'Yes,' she whispered. 'We were married about six years ago.'

'Six years and three months,' Johnnie corrected, and she turned to him, wonder shining in her eyes for an instant. He remembered!

'I could hardly forget,' he went on, as if she'd spoken her thought aloud. 'Thirteen months of life imprisonment and five years and two months of freedom.'

The light within died, and she felt cold, bereaved. He could not have made it plainer. Thirteen months of life imprisonment. That was what marriage meant to this man, a man she still loved and always would.

'Married,' Greg repeated, as if by repeating the word he could grasp its significance. 'Cathy, how *could* you?'

'It wasn't difficult at the time. I was young and foolish,' Cathy said quietly.

'No, no, I didn't mean that. I meant how could you deceive me like this? You ought to have told me. I have some rights, after all.'

'Rights? What kind of rights?' Johnnie's voice was deceptively soft.

'Well—I did hope, once, that Cathy and I might have something going for us. My daughter is fond of Cathy. So am I,' Greg muttered.

'I think you should go, Greg,' Cathy said sadly. 'There is nothing to be gained by going over and over the same ground.'

'No, I suppose not.' Without any more argument,

Greg let himself out, the clash of the door echoing in the half-empty house.

'I'll go, too,' Cathy said. Her head ached, the tears had ruined her make-up, and she was cold still. She felt as if she would never be warm again. Now her secret was out, there would be gossip, back-biting. Staff Nurse Elliott would have a field day. 'Did you know Sister Grainger and Dr Kirkland were once married? Fancy that! Who would have thought it? You never can tell with those quiet ones!'

Cathy could hear the conversations in her head, knew which members of staff would gossip, and which of them would merely treat her to inquisitive looks when they thought she wasn't aware of them.

'Don't go, Cathy. Stay with me.' Johnnie's eyes begged her to stay, but she could not. He had no right to ask it of her. The tears helped, but they could not wash away the memories which haunted her still.

'Cathy?' Johnnie's voice broke into her troubled thoughts, and she turned her sad hazel-green eyes on him. Without a word, he opened his arms and Cathy suddenly realised that heaven lay in that direction.

He needed her! Wanted her. He did not love her but at that moment it did not appear to matter. Someone who needs you is irresistible. Whatever her Johnnie needed, she could supply. With a cry, almost of anguish, she threw herself into his arms and he held her close, murmuring endearments.

She felt his heartbeat quicken, until it was racing in unison with her own. They needed each other. And perhaps out of this need would grow love. One never knew.

They made love on the rug in the sittingroom. With a wicked grin, Johnnie apologised for the lack of a bed.

Cathy's lips curved into a smile of pure joy, as she held out her arms once more. For a pillow, they used her furry stole. Johnnie got a huge duvet out of the airing-cupboard to throw over themselves.

Sighing blissfully, Cathy snuggled closer to Johnnie, the warmth of his body and the duvet combining to send her to sleep.

Cathy slept late into the morning. The sun was well up and shining in the window when she awoke.

She ached deliciously. With a happy smile, she stretched and yawned, memory of the night warming her. She was alone in the makeshift bed. Her clothes were, predictably, scattered all over the floor, and reluctantly she uncurled herself from the cocoon of the duvet and began to gather together her undies.

Still naked, she padded into the kitchen, calling Johnnie's name softly. Uncertainly, she called again, louder this time. Uneasy now, she wrapped the duvet about her slight figure and went right through the house, calling his name. Foolishly, she went on calling even when she knew without doubt that the house was empty.

Her watch had stopped, but according to the carriage-clock, it was past ten o'clock and she ought to have been on duty two hours ago!

The telephone wasn't connected so she hurriedly showered and dressed, then gazed down at her pretty red party-dress. Much too dressy for ten a.m. as she had a good walk to the telephone.

Inspired, she went through the airing-cupboard, hoping she might find something more suitable to wear. True, Johnnie's jeans would be too big, but worn with a loose-fitting shirt they might not be so bad. She would not attract as much attention as she would in a bright red evening dress and fur wrap.

Her hand touched an item of clothing as she searched for a shirt and she put it aside, then paused. Tossing clothes aside as hurriedly as Johnnie did, she found the item again, a pretty pink cardigan, a woman's cardigan!

Horrified, she found a few more items of female clothing as she turned out the whole of the cupboard. Not just female but feminine with a capital 'F'. Wispy, delicate blouses, a soft angora twin-set, a jumper threaded with lace. All much too fussy for her own tastes, but pretty nevertheless.

Aghast, she stared at the items spread over the floor. Women's clothing! Lea's clothing! They must be unless he had another girlfriend tucked away somewhere. She wouldn't put it past him.

And to think she had lain in his arms last night, believing she could supply all his needs, foolishly believing they could begin again, that he might come to love her in time.

She was the world's biggest fool and she told herself so. Fool, fool. She repeated the word until it finally sank in. Knowing Johnnie as she did, knowing of old his duplicity, she'd forgiven him and conveniently forgotten that a leopard never changed its spots!

He must have laughed all night. Come to think of it, he *had* chuckled to himself as she lay in his arms. She'd imagined it to be because he was happy, because she had made him happy.

Livid, she stuffed the clothing back into the airing-cupboard any old how, then a thought struck her. For one glorious moment she thought that it was meant for her! A sort of second-honeymoon gift. They looked new.

But that was stupid. Johnnie was never one for lavish gifts.

Nevertheless . . . With hands that trembled she pulled out a blouse and glanced at the size label. It wasn't for her. It was a size too big.

Methodically, she sorted through the items again. They were all the same size but were very definitely not intended for Cathy Grainger. They would, she judged, fit Lea Adams very nicely except for the length, Lea being quite a bit taller.

Unable to find anything in the cupboard, other than a shirt of his which was miles too big, she forced her tired legs up the stairs again, knowing there was a chest of drawers in the main bedroom, even if he hadn't got around to buying the bed yet.

With any luck she would find some more of Lea's clothes there and she felt perfectly justified in borrowing any that took her fancy.

She was in luck. Although Johnnie had no wardrobes as yet, one drawer of the chest held women's clothing—frilly blouses, a pair of culottes. There was nothing Cathy fancied except the culottes, and she would not have considered them to Lea's taste, either, but she didn't know the woman that well. No matter, they would be only one size too big and probably too long.

She hurriedly chose a pretty blue over-blouse. It went with the culottes as did the cardigan she fished from the very bottom of the drawer. It was creased, though apparently new, and she would have liked to iron it, but she must get to the phone.

Johnnie might well have telephoned to say she would be late. That thought belatedly occurred to her as she ran downstairs, and she looked about for a note. She didn't find it at first, then something drew her eyes to the shelved partition. There was a row of books on the bottom shelf, and a sheet of white paper protruded from one of the books.

Wondering why she hadn't noticed it before, and muttering crossly to herself, she snatched it up. 'Sorry. Round-day. Had to go. Have phoned and reported you sick. Meet me for lunch at Charlotte's at one.' It was signed merely with his initials. J. K.—as though it were a business memo.

If he had strolled in at that moment, Cathy would cheerfully have killed him! He'd used her, just as in the years gone by. Slaked his pressing sexual urges on Cathy then spent time and money on courting other girls. It was just as Brenda said.

Cathy could not blame Brenda for latterly falling for his charm. It was all too easy to do so.

'Meet me for lunch at Charlotte's.' That was a select restaurant miles out of the town, where they were unlikely to bump into any hospital people. It was where she and Johnnie had celebrated their engagement so long ago.

Tears welled up and angrily she brushed them aside. He was really laying it on thickly this time. I'll take her to

Charlotte's, he must have thought. That will soften her up. She'll come over all dewy-eyed and romantic and we can continue where we left off five years ago.

Well, Dr Kirkland, you are in for an unwelcome surprise! Cathy's eyes were wet with tears, but she vowed he would never make her cry again. She was about to teach him a lesson he would never forget!

CHAPTER TEN

CATHY was early, and Charlotte's restaurant was almost empty. She sat in the elegant bar with its black velvet and gilt furniture, sipping an orange juice while she waited for Johnnie.

Earlier, she'd taken a taxi back to the Annexe, changed into her own clothes, carefully wrapping the blue outfit in brown paper and tying it up neatly. The parcel she intended to present to Johnnie at the restaurant. With any luck it would ruin his appetite! Discovery of the clothing had certainly ruined hers.

She was dressed now in a quiet grey skirt and sleeveless jacket, with a severely plain pink blouse and black accessories. Unthinkingly, she'd replaced Johnnie's locket but wore no other jewellery. Her hair she'd brushed until it shone, half-wishing she hadn't had it cut, thinking wistfully of her shoulder-length, honey-coloured hair of a few years ago. She ought to have left it. She could always have swept it back into a chignon or even a bun, for work.

But cutting it was symbolic. She'd cut away her ties with the past, with Johnnie, when she decided on short hair. She was no longer the feminine little slip of a girl Johnnie had wanted, married, then discarded. Sweet Mrs Catherine Kirkland no longer existed.

Nervously, she fiddled with a button on her jacket as she waited. It would be just like him to forget.

'Don't frown, darling. Wrinkles come soon enough.'

With a start, she glanced up, all her good intentions deserting her as she gazed into Johnnie's eyes. Those pale blue eyes were icy no longer. They seemed to glow. Another woman might imagine they glowed with love, even tenderness, but Cathy knew him better than that. He was laughing at her.

There, she was right. A mocking half-smile moved across his sensuous mouth, then was gone as he sensed her mental withdrawal.

He frowned, handsome even when he did that. 'Come along. Lunch is about ready, Cath.' He held out a hand and, with a tired smile, Cathy let him help her up.

She wouldn't create a scene here. Not yet. Let him turn his charm on a little more. Let him bask in his own self-esteem, preen himself, believing she'd swallowed the bait. Then she would tell him a few home truths! She ought to be looking forward to that but somehow she wasn't. Bitchiness was never in her nature and she'd never deliberately set out to hurt another human being, even one as rotten to the core as Johnnie Kirkland. But it had to be done. If once she weakened, she was done for.

Of course she could eat hardly anything, but dutifully worked her way through the prawn cocktail, which slipped down easily enough. She let Johnnie choose the main course for her, knowing he would pick steak. She preferred vegetarian dishes, wholefoods whenever possible, but that was a taste she'd acquired since the break-up. She did enjoy chicken occasionally but she really couldn't be bothered what was placed before her today.

He did not comment when she pushed her virtually

untouched meat away. She'd managed a spoonful of peas and carrots, but even they were too much for her. She refused a pudding but accepted wine, a red full-bodied wine which she sipped sparingly. She didn't want to over-indulge, it might blunt the edge of her sharp tongue!

She would have to work at having a sharp tongue. It was alien to her nature. She'd changed but it was Johnnie's doing. He was the one who'd wrought the changes. Even her own father might not recognise her now.

Sharp pain shot through her at memory of his so-recent death, a needless death. He'd been a workaholic. Rather like Johnnie, who worked hard, and was still in the hospital long after hours. He'd always been like that. As far as his hospital work was concerned, he was a dedicated, caring man. Only in his private life did all caring vanish, leaving only the dedication—dedication to having a good time.

'Well, let's have it Cathy.' He sounded dispirited, tense even. Gone was the warm smile as though he had suddenly remembered that she was of no account. He didn't need to waste his charm on little Cathy.

'Have what?' she parried, her eyes revealing her rage.

He spread his hands in a helpless gesture, then poured himself more wine after she'd refused another drink. 'Whatever is on your mind, let's thrash it out. Been going over my past faults, have you?' he asked, bitterly, tossing back the wine as though it was water.

'We all have faults,' she said carefully, wanting to put off the confrontation for as long as possible.

'Great! The perfect Cathy Grainger finally admits she has a few faults.' He twirled his wine-glass round and round, but otherwise his suppressed anger did not show. Only Cathy, who knew him so well, realised what burned within.

'I brought you a present,' she said flatly, placing the brown-paper package on the table. Their eyes met, and his lips tightened.

'What is it? Not a spitting cobra, I hope?' he enquired with mock politeness.

Carefully, Cathy unwrapped one corner so that he could see the blue blouse, cardigan and culottes. 'I found them in your drawer. I had to borrow them because I couldn't dash out to phone for a taxi in my party-gown,' she went on in the same dull, flat voice.

He stared at the parcel, fingering the blouse gently. 'It's pretty. Blue always was your colour.'

'*My* colour?' she exploded. 'They aren't mine, Johnnie. I found them in the drawers in your bedroom. They belong to your fancy-woman!' With an effort, she kept her voice low despite her anger. 'I borrowed them, as I've already said. Now I'm returning them. You never know, she might miss them when she comes back.'

He glanced at her angry face, then shrugged. 'No, she won't miss them. She won't be coming back,' he said quietly. 'I'll drive you home,' he went on, getting up and walking away while she sat, bewildered.

She roused herself by the time he'd paid, then followed him out into the small car-park. Nothing had gone as planned. She'd meant to hurt him, expose him for the womaniser he was, perhaps even get him to confess that the garments belonged to Lea. Instead, she found herself feeling sorry for him, ashamed at herself for hurting him.

That was Johnnie all over. He could turn any situation to his advantage.

Meekly, she sat beside him as the Mercedes ate up the miles. What was it he'd said about the owner of the clothes? 'She won't be coming back.' Why wouldn't she? Perhaps they did not belong to Lea. Perhaps they were her predecessor's. Lea must be on holiday as Cathy hadn't seen her around the hospital.

Was the owner of the clothing Lea's predecessor or her successor? It was of academic interest only, but it kept Cathy's mind occupied on the journey. She would like to know. Then she could picture the woman, build up an impression in her mind. Johnnie Kirkland's ideal woman. What must this ideal possess? Blonde hair, almost certainly. Blue or green eyes. She ought to be tall and curvy. But she must have long legs. Johnnie was a leg-man.

'Here we are. Safe and sound. Untouched by hand from the moment it leaves the cane till it runs into our bags,' he quipped, and Cathy clenched her small fists.

'Untouched is hardly a word I would use!' she snapped. 'Not after last night.'

'Ah, yes. Last night. Good, wasn't it? I thought so,' he went on, and her blood boiled.

'You mean you thought *you* were good. You always thought so even when you were mediocre,' she said, crushingly.

He flinched, turning tormented pale eyes on her. 'Wasn't it good, then? Am I losing my touch, Cathy?' His eyes begged her to praise his virility, restore his ego to its former position, but she would not.

She shrugged. 'I've known worse.'

It was the wrong thing to say, and Johnnie lunged at her and started to shake her.

'Johnnie! For pity's sake!' She was sobbing when he let her go.

'What did you mean, you've known worse? Have you had bearded wonder in your bed? He said you were good. I heard him!' When she didn't reply, he repeated the question. 'Have you, Cathy? Answer me.'

'Why don't you get a torch and shine it in my eyes?' she sobbed. 'Interrogate me properly. Don't let's have any half-measures!'

Without a word he handed her a large white hankie and she dabbed at her swollen eyes. 'Blow your nose, Cathy. You can keep the clothes, if you want. The girl I bought them for didn't appreciate them.' He was staring through the windscreen, his lean hands clenched on the steering-wheel, and she couldn't see his expression.

'I told you!' she choked out. 'I only borrowed them.'

'Blue always was your best colour,' he said sadly. 'Goodbye, Cathy.'

'Why goodbye? Not leaving Bellington District, so soon, are you?' She tried to sound bitchy, but failed utterly.

'No, but I'm leaving the Annexe. The rest of my furniture arrives tomorrow and I'll move into Graingers then.' He opened his mouth and seemed about to say more, then closed it tightly.

'Goodbye, Johnnie,' she whispered, getting out of the car.

Without a backward glance, he drove away, and a distraught Cathy watched him go, her tear-stained face mute witness to her distress.

As she hurried back towards the Annexe she caught a glimpse of the tall, uniformed figure of Staff Nurse Elliott. She could well have seen Cathy crying in Johnnie's car, must certainly have seen Cathy's tear-ravaged face and the coldness of Johnnie's goodbye. Cathy hoped it pleased the girl. As for herself, she simply wanted to curl up and die. Without Johnnie life was meaningless.

'Are you better, Sister?' Nursing Officer Snow's voice came from nowhere, and all the colour left Cathy's face as the woman's tall, angular figure moved into the light. It was the next morning, Cathy's last on duty before her days off.

'Yes, thank you, Miss Snow. As better as I ever will be,' Cathy replied woodenly, and Miss Snow's grey brows drew together in a frown.

'If you don't pull yourself together, Sister, you may not have a job much longer,' she warned, and Cathy's heart sank.

'I've already told Matron that my private life is my own business,' she said, with a calmness she was far from feeling, and the Nursing Officer snorted.

'Rubbish! A senior nurse's life is never her own business. You must learn that, to your cost. It is certainly no business of mine. But what goes on in the surgical unit *is* my business. For the moment, anyway,' she added, sounding tired.

'I'm sorry. My being sick yesterday must have added to your burdens.' Cathy liked Miss Snow, a tireless bustling type of woman. Frosty-faced and harsh she might be at times, but she had a heart of gold.

'It didn't help. You will have to act-up this afternoon as it's my free afternoon. But that's by the way.'

The Number Seven bustled away, leaving a perplexed Cathy to stroll onto Ward Three. Everyone by now must have heard that she was once Mrs Johnnie Kirkland. Though Greg might have kept it to himself. She hadn't given him credit for much sensitivity, but that was unkind of her. Johnnie naturally would not mention it, until it suited him to do so.

Apparently she was right and Greg Abbott hadn't mentioned her marriage. Certainly, there was something wrong on the ward, but she didn't think it had anything to do with her private life.

Aileen O'Connor was still there, now coping well, and soon after Cathy had heard the night nurse's report she went to say good morning to the patients, making Aileen her first call.

She glanced up reproachfully. 'Sister, how could you? Standing up poor Cousin Michael like that?'

Cathy hesitated, unwilling to divulge too much. 'I'm sorry, Aileen, but I was called away. I'll ring Michael today and apologise.'

'Staff Nurse said you were spending a dirty night with a consultant,' Aileen went on, guilelessly, and Cathy went scarlet.

'Was she there, do you suppose?' she asked, icily. 'The fly on the wall, perhaps?'

Aileen giggled. 'A very big fly! More like a vulture, Sister!'

Cathy suppressed a smile. She mustn't encourage a patient to talk like that about one of her colleagues, but the comparison was not inapt. 'That will do, Aileen. If you see Michael before I do, get him to pop into the office.'

'He won't do that, Sister. Staff Nurse Vulture has forbidden him. He can come to see me, but that's all. None of this coffee and biscuits nonsense. That's what she said to one of the juniors. I heard her.'

'When Staff Nurse is in charge of the ward it is up to her, Aileen. I can't *order* her to serve coffee to your cousin,' Cathy said lightly, then continued her round.

There was only one new admission, a lady with gall-bladder trouble, and Cathy spent some time with her. Mrs Dunster was admitted the previous day but as they talked, Cathy came to the conclusion that no-one had bothered to let the woman voice her fears, her dread of the coming operation.

Mrs Dunster chatted on, the words spilling over one another in their hurry, and Cathy let her get on with it, merely smiling and nodding whenever the woman paused for breath. She was adamant now that she would not sign the consent form for the anaesthetic, thereby declining the operation, and after the first torrent of words, Cathy tried to reason with her. They were still talking when an irate Mr Redford knocked on the window of the office.

Puzzled, Cathy hurried to the ward-office, wondering what the consultant wanted.

'Didn't you know I was doing a round this morning, Sister? Surely you couldn't forget me!'

'No, of course not, sir.' Cathy's manner was flustered, most unlike her usual self, as she turned to the SEN, who looked as puzzled as she was.

'I have been on holiday, Sister Grainger. This is my

first day here and I know of no ward-round,' SEN Sayers told her, firmly.

'Staff Nurse knew,' Mr Redford said crossly. Outside the office, his registrar and the house-doctor shuffled their feet awkwardly. There were two other young men there and the consultant told her they were medical students who were at the District for the week.

'Been showing them my techniques,' the old doctor went on proudly. 'Now just when I boast about the efficiency of Ward Three *and* its ward Sister, you let me down!'

She soon had him placated, for he was rather a pet lamb and she was genuinely fond of him. The ward-round was swiftly organised and she managed to answer all the questions he threw out at random. The new patient she didn't know well, but after the round she told him about the woman's fear. Mrs Dunster herself hadn't voiced any of her fears to Mr Redford, just lay in bed with a resigned smile on her face.

'You and your emotional needs of the patient!' he laughed. 'Still, if she isn't prepared, perhaps we should postpone it, do you think? Eh?' He winked at Cathy, and she knew it wasn't a serious suggestion.

'I'll work on her, sir,' she promised.

They were having coffee in the office when Michael appeared in the doorway. 'Aha! Michael, me boy! Just in time for coffee. I think there's a chocolate biscuit left,' Mr Redford said jovially, but Michael shook his head, his eyes on Cathy.

Excusing herself she followed him out into the corridor where, with people coming and going, they would be virtually unnoticed.

They both spoke at once, then Cathy, hardly daring to meet his gaze, apologised for standing him up. 'It . . . it was unavoidable. Believe me, Michael. He left me no choice at all,' she went on, bitterly.

'I understand. He's quite a guy. Been trying to diagnose me, he has,' Michael said softly. 'He has decided I am a hopeless case of unrequited love! And he told me I was lucky to be alive. If my unrequited love was for a certain Mrs Cathy Kirkland, he would have killed me on the spot.'

'That's typical of the man,' Cathy snapped. 'Thinks he's God's gift to women.'

'I've told you before, Cathy dear. He can't be, because I am! Let's talk about Sandra now,' he went on, seriously.

'To be perfectly honest, Michael, I can't think what you see in the girl!' Cathy said bluntly. 'She hasn't anything going for her that I can see!' And now your girlfriend has landed me in the soup with the consultant surgeon, she wanted to add, but did not.

'Beauty is in the eye of the beholder, Cathy dear,' he said reprovingly. 'We had a little misunderstanding and not all my Irish charm will solve the problem. She thinks I had designs on your comely Welsh friend and . . .'

'Peggy? That would be an explosive combination!' Cathy laughed.

'Ah, I know that, you know that, and probably Peggy does too, but convincing Sandra is another matter.'

'I thought it was me you fancied. You've broken my heart, Michael!' she said lightly, still wondering how a charming man like that could fancy the temperamental and bitchy Sandra Elliott. It took all sorts.

Cathy could see no way of helping Michael over his problem, other than encouraging Staff Nurse to entertain him on the ward. She was still puzzling over it as she hurried back to her office. If Michael intended marrying the girl, his life would not be worth living, but it was no use trying to tell him that. Obviously, he did not see the bitchy side of Sandra Elliott's nature. She pitied him but pitied herself more. Now she had lost everything she held dear.

That afternoon, though still in charge of Ward Three, she carried a bleep because she was acting-up as a Nursing Officer again. With that, she could be summoned quickly if anything went wrong on any of the other surgical wards.

The bleep went just as she was teaching the first-year student. She was wanted on male surgical. As she walked briskly away she met Sandra Elliott, coming back from an outing, presumably.

For once, the Staff Nurse looked presentable in a smart blue dress and jacket, her hair flowing loose, and Cathy caught a glimpse of the woman she *could* be if she worked at it.

Sandra Elliott was about to sweep by without a word and Cathy had no time to stop, but she managed to grab hold of Sandra's jacket as they passed each other.

Sandra swung round, her eyes blazing defiance at Cathy.

'I'll see you on the ward tomorrow, Staff Nurse,' Cathy said tightly, before hurrying away without a backward glance. She wasn't on duty the next day but she intended to catch the girl after the report. There had to be a 'truth session' as her old tutor called it, sooner or later. Things were getting out of hand.

But it was Cathy herself who was hauled over the coals the following morning, not Sandra.

For once Mrs Walton did not ask her to sit, and Cathy stood almost at attention, her hands clashed firmly in front of her. Because she was off-duty she was in civvies and had chosen a plain grey suit, one which made her look neat and efficient even if it did nothing for her figure or her morale.

'I simply cannot understand how you could be so lax, Sister Grainger,' Matron was saying. 'You, of all people. I had great hopes for you. You were climbing the ladder fast.' She broke off, then lifted her angry, set face to Cathy's.

Cathy waited, wondering if there was more or if she could now defend herself. She found herself thinking of Johnnie, wondering where he was at that precise moment. She loved him. A career wasn't everything. Even if the PNO tried to get her dismissed for incompetence, it would not be the end of the world.

She knew now that whilst life with Johnnie was unbearable at times, life without him was unbearable all the time. She would forgive him, go back to him, if he promised to throw out that other girl's clothes. It was little enough to ask, surely? Whatever he did, whatever she suspected, she was determined not to nag as she'd done in the past. If he was content by his own fireside, in his own bed, he wouldn't want to roam.

In theory it was simple enough, but with Johnnie nothing was ever that simple!

Mrs Walton cleared her throat, and Cathy brought her mind back to the present. 'Staff Nurse told me quite clearly—and I believe her—that she informed you of Mr Redford's unexpected ward-round. She slipped a note under your door the night before last.'

Cathy flushed. 'If she says so, Matron, then she must have done. Unfortunately it must have rolled under something because I certainly never saw it.'

'Well, that may be the case, Sister. She ought to have left a message in the ward diary as well. And that she did not do because I have inspected the diary myself. She had the grace to apologise for her omission.'

'Oh, good,' Cathy said tartly, aware that it was making matters worse.

'Whatever the personality difficulties between you, Staff Nurse *is* an efficient nurse. You said so yourself,' Mrs Walton pointed out, sharply.

'In this case she wasn't as efficient as usual, Matron,' Cathy said firmly, 'She knew quite well I was out that evening because she sent Mr Abbott to find me. He wanted help with a party he's planning for his daughter, and Staff Nurse knew where I was.'

'Where were you, as a matter of interest, Sister?'

Cathy hesitated, then mentally shrugged. 'I was at Dr Kirkland's house. He was showing me over it.'

'Was he, indeed?' Cathy blushed at the implication behind Matron's remark, but held her tongue. 'Then there was the missing drug,' Mrs Walton went on, slowly. 'Mrs Smith mentioned that to you, of course?'

'She did,' Cathy agreed. 'The drugs were in order last

time I checked. Presumably someone dropped a pill on the floor and couldn't find it.'

'No-one has come forward to say so,' Matron pointed out. 'There is also the case of those three students who held the sit-in—apparently with *your* permission.'

Cathy opened her mouth to defend herself, but Mrs Walton frowned. 'I haven't quite finished, Sister. In addition, I feel you spend too much time talking to patients and not enough time on administrative work or on ward-teaching. This makes extra work for the other trained nurses,' she added, which Cathy considered most unfair. She did her share of ward chores.

'Patients *need* someone to talk to, Matron. Someone with knowledge and experience, not just an auxiliary or a first-year. They need to talk out their fears.'

Matron nodded in agreement. 'But it doesn't always have to be the ward sister. An experienced staff nurse would do just as well.'

'Staff Nurse Elliott isn't interested in people,' Cathy said bitterly. 'You said as much quite recently,' she went on, recalling the occasion when Sandra had complained of so-called 'victimization'.

'This conversation is getting us nowhere, Sister,' Mrs Walton said sharply, not liking her judgment criticised, and Cathy could have bitten out her tongue.

If you defended yourself you were in the wrong. If you didn't, it was automatically considered a sign of guilt.

It was decided that Cathy should take her week's holiday immediately, as originally arranged, rather than put it back until Nursing Officer Burn returned. After that . . . Cathy simply did not know. There was a big question mark against her name.

Mrs Walton made an appointment to see Cathy upon her return from holiday, and a dejected Cathy left the office, not knowing what the future might hold.

Now there was no point in seeking out Staff Nurse Elliott. She'd told her lies, baited her trap with innuendo, tales of victimization. Whatever Cathy said or did now would be suspect if it concerned Sandra Elliott, so it was better to leave matters as they were.

On her return to her flat, Cathy went over every inch of the poky kitchen, searching for the note Staff Nurse had supposedly pushed under the door. There was no sign of any note but Cathy hadn't expected there would be.

Heartbroken at the thought that she might have to leave the hospital she loved, Cathy packed her few belongings. She would go home for her week's leave. She didn't particularly want to, nor did she want to spend the week in an hotel somewhere, but anything was better than being cooped up in the Annexe.

There was no hurry, she would have lunch first. Worry took away her appetite and she settled for a glass of milk and an apple. She was reading the *Nursing Mirror* when a nurse tapped at her door and said she was to see the PNO immediately.

Almost past caring, she finished her apple, and took her time going over to the hospital. In the corridor she passed one or two people she knew, and she greeted them pleasantly, trying not to show that she was in disgrace.

What, she wondered, had she done now?

Mrs Walton rose when Cathy hesitantly entered the office, and came forward, hand outstretched. Feeling as if she were in a disjointed dream, Cathy shook hands, then her tired legs almost collapsed under her as Mrs Walton drew a chair forward for her.

'Why the fatted calf, Matron?' she asked, unable to keep the bitterness from her voice.

It was Mrs Walton's turn to flush. 'There has been a misunderstanding. Crossed wires, if you like. I want to apologise, Sister. Naturally you must take your holiday as arranged, then Sister Davies will be back and you can resume your acting-up duties as a Number Seven on your return.'

'Thank you very much, Matron,' Cathy said dryly. 'Has Staff Nurse confessed all?' That must be the reason for Matron's about-face, but knowing Sandra Elliott, it seemed unlikely.

'No, but a reliable informant assures me there was no note pushed under your door that evening because he was there all the time,' the PNO admitted, and Cathy's heart rose.

Michael. It must be. Somehow he had heard about Cathy's disgrace and knew his girlfriend was responsible. Of course, he wasn't in her flatlet that evening, but he had come to her rescue. More than Johnnie would have done, she mused, as she was ushered from the room.

Dear Michael. Perhaps now he would see Staff Nurse as she really was. Cathy certainly hoped so.

But when she approached a rather poorly-looking Michael he denied all knowledge of the matter. From his manner it was obvious he found it hard to believe his beloved would behave in such a way.

'More than likely it was Johnnie. I saw him and Matron deep in conversation in the coffee-lounge at lunch-time,' Michael threw in casually, and Cathy went white.

Not Johnnie! *He* wouldn't stand up for her. Why should he? She was always quick enough to believe rumours about him, she acknowledged unhappily. She jumped to conclusions, accepted other people's estimation of his character, never giving the man a chance to defend himself.

She saw now how horribly wrong she'd been in the past. What if Brenda Chalmer's accusations were lies, as well? She had accepted Brenda's word at face value, trusted *her* more than she had her own husband. As Johnnie said, the more Brenda blamed herself, the more Cathy blamed *him*.

Even if Johnnie no longer wanted her, she owed him an apology, at the very least. Pride or no pride, she would apologise, then wish him happiness with Lea or whoever else he chose to share his life.

The trouble with her good resolution was that she couldn't find the man in question. Dr Kirkland was, the hall porter told her, on leave for two weeks. Therefore, he ought to be at Graingers—Cathy tried to contact him twice but could get no reply. She had even wandered around the back of the house, thinking he might have developed an interest in gardening, but there was no sign of him anywhere.

Perhaps he had gone to bring back his girlfriend, the one to whom the clothing belonged. Maybe they had settled their differences and were together again, just as Staff Nurse Elliott and Dr Curtin were.

Cathy had seen those two lovebirds hand in hand in the nearby park. She was glad for Michael. He wasn't well and if the abrasive Sandra Elliott could make him happy, so much the better. Cathy felt that when she returned to duty her relationship with the Staff Nurse would be a happier one. She herself was prepared to forgive and forget, for the sake of the patients, though it would not be easy. Only time would tell if the relationship would hold.

Not wanting to leave the vicinity of the hospital until she had seen Johnnie, Cathy hung around for another day, driving past his house several times, hoping for a glimpse of him, but in vain.

Then she bumped into Leonora Adams, who said she didn't know where Johnnie was, that she'd lost interest in the man, but she'd heard that he was in a clinic in London, recuperating from surgery.

'Surgery?' Cathy had echoed, but Lea had moved on, and Cathy was left to make frustrating enquiries where she could.

As far as she could tell, Johnnie Kirkland had vanished from the face of the earth, or certainly from the area around the District hospital.

Later that day, when a distressed Cathy returned from yet another fruitless visit to Johnnie's house, she found Greg Abbott waiting for her. A casually dressed Greg Abbott, as clean but as scruffy as ever.

'Whatever happened to your suave businessman image?' she asked, having invited him in for coffee.

'Oh, that.' He stroked his beard, avoiding her gaze. 'I . . . she was married.'

'Married?' Then the penny dropped. He was talking about her! 'Oh, Greg, I'm so sorry,' she began, but he went on as if she hadn't spoken:

'Nice little thing, too. She was Emma's music teacher. She's helping me arrange the party since you seem otherwise engaged. I thought Emma said she was a widow, but there you are,' he laughed, a sad sound, but Cathy's smile was anything but sad.

He'd fallen for another woman, and all the time she thought his new-found smartness was for her benefit!

'Heard about Kirkland, I suppose? Him being your ex-husband,' Greg went on, and Cathy's blood ran cold.

'He isn't my ex-husband, Greg. We never got around to divorce,' she said quietly. 'I never wanted a divorce. I loved him, I still do.' She took a deep breath. 'Tell me the worst, Greg. I can take it.'

'Thought you knew. Hell of a way to find out,' he muttered.

'Find out *what*?'

'Had a serious op in some private clinic, I believe. He's recuperating at home.'

Cathy shook her head. 'No, he isn't. I've just come from there. What has he had done? Is it . . . is it his heart?' She held her breath, waiting.

He shrugged. 'No idea. It was just a rumour I heard. You know the grapevine as well as I do. They may have got it all wrong.'

She got rid of Greg as hastily as possible, then hurried out to her Mini. She would drive past Graingers again. Johnnie might be on his way home now. If anything should happen to him she would never, never forgive herself. Let him be a rake, she didn't care any more. If Johnnie was happy, so was she. Oh, please, let him recover, she repeated again and again as she drove.

The front-door of Graingers stood open, and Cathy ran up the path, half expecting to find a private nurse in attendance on a deathly-pale Johnnie Kirkland.

She searched the house, now fully furnished, but without avail, finally running Johnnie to ground on the patio at the rear. He was as dark and as robustly healthy-looking as ever, and Cathy checked her headlong rush, which would have carried her into his arms.

'Someone said you were very ill,' she murmured, her heart breaking because she wanted to touch him and could not. He would rebuff her.

'Is that what they say? Amazing how these rumours get around, isn't it?' he said blandly.

'Johnnie! Did you spread the rumour?' she asked, accusingly, hardly able to believe he would be so unprofessional.

He shook his head, frowning a little. 'Hardly. I've been to see Marguerite, as a matter of fact. I also spent a few days at a clinic in London—as an observer, not a patient. Friend of mine runs it. I suppose the hall porter put two and two together and made half a dozen of it!' he finished wryly.

Then those brilliant ice-blue eyes glinted, kindling a fire in her own eyes.

With a sob of relief, she hurled herself into his arms and clung tightly. Gathering her up, he carried her indoors and up to the master bedroom. The bed was king-size but modern.

'You didn't buy Lea's tester bed then? Did . . .' She paused, for it was a painful subject. 'Did your other girlfriend choose this bed, Johnnie? I have to know. Just tell me that and I promise I won't mention it again.'

Fearfully she met his gaze. Whatever he said, whatever happened, she would not nag.

'Lea was a friend, no more. I have no other girlfriend, not now,' he assured her, stopping further questions with his lips.

When she could speak again, she badly wanted to ask about the girlfriend, the one who went away, but knew she must not. If Johnnie wanted her to know, he would tell her in his own good time.

Still unhappy about the other woman, Cathy nevertheless gave her love unreservedly, her body throbbing with her need for Johnnie. He kissed every inch of her he could, then slowly began to undress her, taking his time, prolonging the ecstasy, the final moment when they would join together again, two people who ought never to have been parted.

'You looked good in those culottes,' he murmured, kissing her breasts.

All desire left her, and she opened her eyes, sad hazel eyes that began to fill with tears. 'Did you have to mention the clothes, Johnnie?' she whispered, hurt beyond cure. 'I wasn't going to. I made a vow not to nag you again about . . . about other women.'

'There *have* been other women, my love,' he acknowledged. 'A man like me couldn't be expected to spend five years as a celibate monk! But they were just to fill a need. Little Cathy Grainger is the only girl I ever loved.'

'You love me?' she asked wonderingly, and he seemed surprised.

'Why, of course I love you! I adore you, sweetheart. It's taken me a long while to catch up with you. I always kept in touch with Marguerite. She kept tabs on you for me, even when I didn't realise I still loved you. She's been a tower of strength. It was she who lent me money in the past "so you can live as my son-in-law should" as she put it! I owe her a lot more than that, too. She nagged me to go on searching for your heart, told me I must persevere until I won. That you were a tough cookie like her and needed a strong, protective male to keep you in line!' He paused to kiss her again, then went on slowly: 'At first my pride wouldn't let me come after you, but when this post came up at the Bellington, I had to have it.'

She sighed, blissfully happy. Then she remembered. She must tell him about the baby—his baby. The almost but not quite baby.

She nibbled her lower lip, anxiously. He would be cross. No, angry. He might believe she . . .

With a choked-off sob, she drew away.

'Cathy? What is it, my darling?' Gently he smoothed back a lock of hair, his eyes infinitely tender, and Cathy was no longer afraid. He would be disappointed, yes, but he would understand. And there might be another baby by this time next year . . .

'It's about the baby,' she murmured drowsily, and Johnnie sat up, clearly astonished.

'*What* baby?' he asked, carefully.

With a little smile, Cathy snuggled up to him. 'We nearly had one. But . . . I miscarried soon after you left. I did want it so much, Johnnie!' she assured him, forcing herself to meet his gaze.

'A baby. We nearly had a baby?' he asked wonderingly, and she nodded. 'We'll have to see if we can repeat the recipe!' he teased, and Cathy's smile deepened.

Nothing else mattered now, not even the women's clothes.

'About those frillies you found,' he murmured, and she ran her fingers down the mat of dark hair on his chest.

'Must you?' she protested, not wanting the moment spoiled.

He kissed her fingers, one by one. 'Yes, I must. They were for you, my little love. Brand-new, they were. Marguerite helped me choose them. They were for the girlfriend who went away—my lovely wife. Did you like them?'

She chuckled. 'I loved them, Johnnie. All of them,' she assured him, before she melted into his waiting arms.

They were a size too big since she had lost so much weight, and much too frilly, but she would never tell him so. If wearing them made her darling Johnnie happy, then wear them she would.

Little Cathy Kirkland was going to learn how to please her husband, starting right now.

Doctor Nurse Romances

Romance in modern medical life

Read more about the lives and loves of doctors and nurses in the fascinatingly different backgrounds of contemporary medicine. These are the four Doctor Nurse romances to look out for next month.

NURSE ON CALL
Leonie Craig
THE GILDED CAGE
Sarah Franklin
A SURGEON CALLED AMANDA
Elizabeth Harrison
VICTORY FOR VICTORIA
Betty Neels

Buy them from your usual paperback stockist, or write to: Mills & Boon Reader Service, P.O. Box 236, Thornton Rd, Croydon, Surrey CR9 3RU, England. Readers in South Africa-write to: Mills & Boon Reader Service of Southern Africa, Private Bag X3010, Randburg, 2125.

Mills & Boon
the rose of romance

How to join in a whole new world of romance

It's very easy to subscribe to the Mills & Boon Reader Service. As a regular reader, you can enjoy a whole range of special benefits. Bargain offers. Big cash savings. Your own free Reader Service newsletter, packed with knitting patterns, recipes, competitions, and exclusive book offers.

We send you the very latest titles each month, postage and packing free – no hidden extra charges. There's absolutely no commitment – you receive books for only as long as you want.

We'll send you details. Simply send the coupon – or drop us a line for details about the Mills & Boon Reader Service Subscription Scheme.
Post to: Mills & Boon Reader Service, P.O. Box 236, Thornton Road, Croydon, Surrey CR9 3RU, England.
*Please note: READERS IN SOUTH AFRICA please write to: Mills & Boon Reader Service of Southern Africa, Private Bag X3010, Randburg 2125, S. Africa.

Please send me details of the Mills & Boon Subscription Scheme.

NAME (Mrs/Miss) _____ EP3

ADDRESS _____

_____

COUNTY/COUNTRY_____ POST/ZIP CODE_____

BLOCK LETTERS, PLEASE

Mills & Boon
the rose of romance